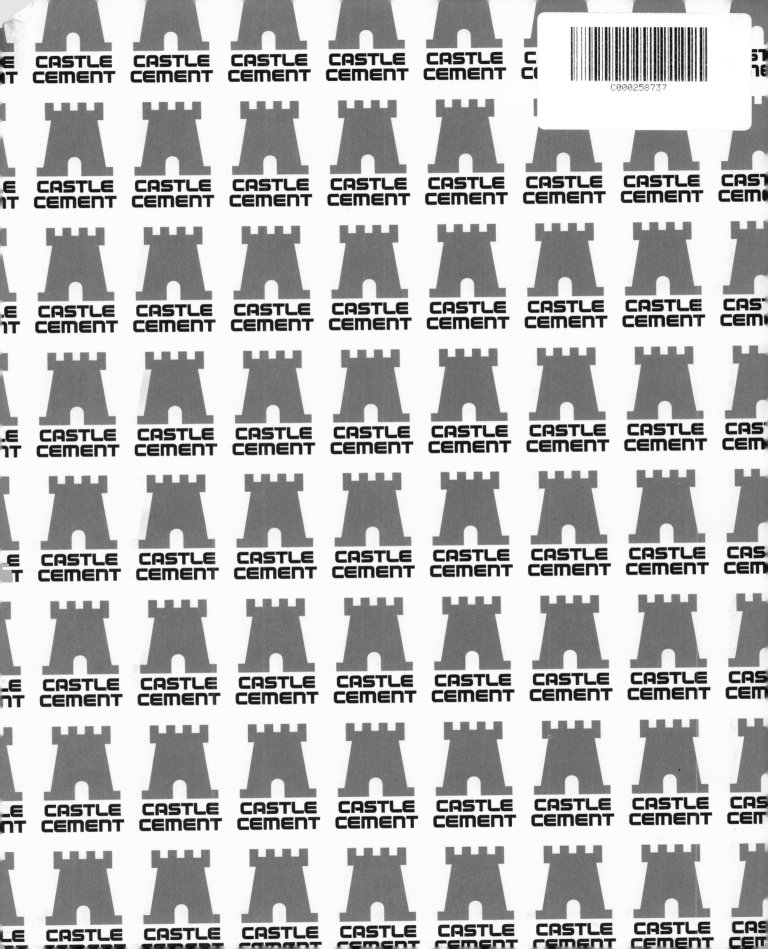

History of Ribblesdale Cement

dedicated to all Ribblesdale employees, past and present

Peter del Strother

MBE, BSc, MBA, MPhil, CEng, MIMechE

Published by
Castle Cement Limited, Clitheroe, Lancashire BB7 4QF

First Edition 2008

ISBN 978-0-9545416-1-3

Designed and produced by Concept, Worcester WR3 8SG and
printed in Great Britain by The Cromwell Press, Trowbridge BA14 0XB
on totally recyclable, biodegradable and acid-free paper
produced from a combination of TCF (Totally Chlorine Free)
and ECF (Elemental Chlorine Free) fibre.

Mixed Sources
Product group from well-managed
forests and other controlled sources
www.fsc.org Cert no. TT-COC-2082
© 1996 Forest Stewardship Council
FSC

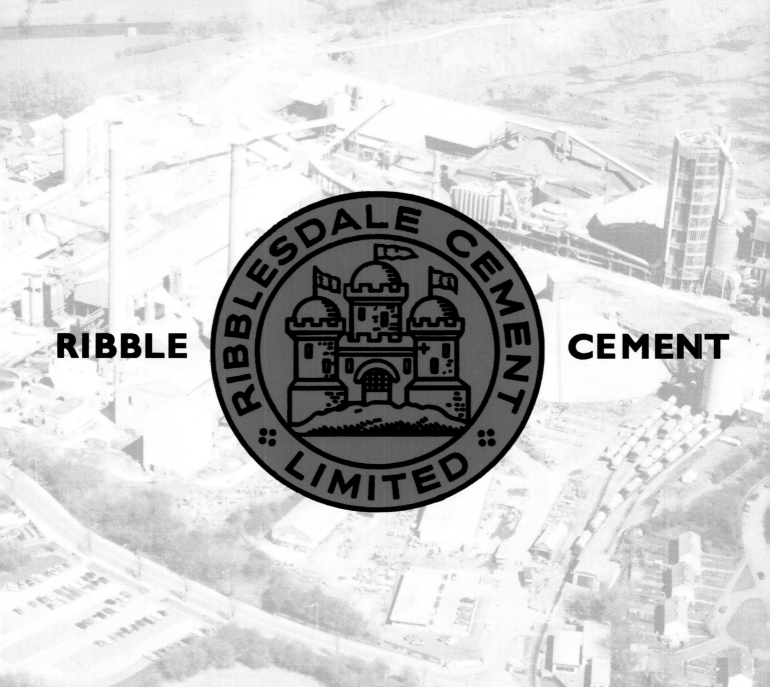

RIBBLE CEMENT

Acknowledgements

It would not have been possible to write this book without the help of many employees, ex-employees and members of the public. Some have told of their experiences, some have lent photographs and all have made valuable contributions. I thank all of them and especially those listed below.

Fred Braithwaite, whose prodigious memory is a legend on the cement works.

The research team of employees and former employees including, Ian Bradley, Wilf Hewitt, Keith Malone, Dave Pomfret, John Ridgway, Brian Turner and Maria Punchard, who also provided a great deal of secretarial support. Dave Pomfret took many of the recent photographs.

Susan Holden and Ruth Hargreaves, librarians at the local history section of Clitheroe Library.

Alan G Crosby MA DPhil FRHistS, archivist.

Mohammed Amin, John Bailey, Les Baker, Richard W F Boarder, Alan Brewer, Bernard Chatburn, Alan Clarke, Lord Clitheroe, Emilio Conti, Nick Dinsdale, Ronnie Evans, Peter Fehrenbach, Peter Geldard, Ken and Marion Gill, W D Green, L Gregory, Dr Graham Hall, Keith Hall, John Haworth, Bob Hargreaves, William Hogg, Maureen Hoyle, Mike Kelly, Kathleen King, Paul Livesey, Amedeo Loi, Mary Miller (Leigh), David Morris, Peter Nerenberg, Dr. Neville, Terry Punchard (via Chris and Maria Punchard), John Ridgway, Craig Ryle, Betty Trueman (daughter of R Y Parkinson), Paul Stevens, Frances and David Tomlinson, Otto Volkmer, June Walker, Eric Walmsley, Brian White and Ian Woolstencroft.

Several people have helped with proof reading. Any errors remaining are my own.

Peter del Strother
June 2008

Contents

Foreword

Burning lime in Clitheroe dates back to Elizabethan times. Over the years the process evolved into cement production, firstly by Ribblesdale Cement and now by Castle Cement.

Following on from an equally thorough history of Ketton Cement, Peter del Strother has managed to create a fascinating and human account of the development of not only a business but of a whole community.

Cement is a vital ingredient in the production of concrete, without which our society would simply not exist in its present form; roads, railways, water treatment facilities all rely upon the strength, longevity and sustainability of concrete. Ribblesdale Cement has remained in the forefront of producing sustainable 'home grown' UK cement from its pioneering use of alternative carbon neutral fuels to its blending and use of recycled materials in both raw feed and finished products.

Castle Cement is committed to continuing to provide low carbon sustainable cement from Ribblesdale for many years to come. Equally we are committed to minimising our impact on the local community and being a good neighbour to all in Clitheroe.

Above all, this is the story of our people in the works and the local community and it is a tribute to them that lime and cement have been produced for so many years and will, we hope, continue to be produced for many years to come.

Mike Eberlin
Managing Director
Castle Cement
June 2008

Chapter 1
Clitheroe and the Ribble Valley

The people of the Ribble valley are accustomed to change but, when our late Bronze Age forebears occupied the fort above Whalley Gap, they could hardly have imagined the two colourful millennia that were to follow.

The Romans built a road along the valley, linking east and west via the fort at Ribchester. The line of the road can be followed on the Ordnance Survey map and in the southern extremity of the land surrounding Bellman quarry some archaeological evidence still survives. Nearby in 1778 a thousand Roman coins were found in an urn. The Vikings used the same road between York and the Lancashire coast as part of an important trading link with Dublin.

The Normans left Clitheroe Castle as a more substantial record of their presence. The Scots controlled north of the river Ribble from 1139 to 1157, so defence must have been a priority. Lime mortar would have been needed for construction of the walls. Although there is no record of the Romans quarrying limestone here, the Normans must have done so. The Castle was partly demolished in 1649 during the Civil War.

Clitheroe Castle

*Fishing club member Carl Ainsworth, with a salmon,
by West Bradford Bridge*

The Cistercian Abbey of Whalley, founded in 1296 and dissolved in 1537, testifies to the prosperity of the Ribble Valley. Land fit for agriculture and rivers full of fish were the foundations of that prosperity and local school children still learn the rhyme,

> 'The Ribble, Calder, Hodder and rain
> Meet together in Mitton's domain'.

The Whalley village symbol contains three fishes, representing the wealth arising from the three rivers mentioned in the rhyme.

During the 16th Century the use of lime as a soil improver was discovered, so no doubt some of the small limekilns scattered about the Ribble valley were originally constructed for agricultural use.

Lime burning in the early days was neither very safe nor environmentally friendly. In 1604, at the Duchy Court in Lancaster in a case 'King versus Inhabitants of Clitheroe', complaints were heard against some of the inhabitants who were lime burning in the town. The decree stated:-

View of works in late 1930s with two kilns in operation.
The single brick chimney is the Isis cement works' stack, demolished in 1939

"…that there were divers buildings within the said burrough or town of late time burned and wasted and decayed by 'mischances of fyer' happening by reason of making lymekylnes and burning lyme within the said burrough to the great loss and hindrance of the inhabitants thereof. And whereas it is hereby also certified that by occasion of burning of lyme on the backsides of the houses of the several inhabitants the same town is not only in danger of fire as aforesaid, but also daily and continually annoyed with smoke thereof being very troublesome and noysome to all the inhabitants of the said burrough in their several houses, and also to the parishioners in the church of Clitheroe, and to His Majesty's auditor when he sitteth in the said Castle upon receipt and accompt of His Highnesses revenues".

The decree banned lime burning in the town and the burgesses "assigned a place within a quarter of a myle of the said towne of Clitheroe called the Friarye bank (Fairy Bank) for the making and burning of lime and lime kilnes, which they affirm to be very fitt and convenient for the purpose".

Fairy Bank is a little closer to Clitheroe than the cement works. It is the field immediately to the north of Coplow Quarry, behind Pimlico cottages.

From 17th to 19th August 1612 the trial of the Pendle witches took place at Lancaster Assizes. The defendants

Rural lime kiln at Cow Ark, probably early 19th Century

were allowed neither counsel nor witnesses to speak in their defence. Thirteen people were committed for trial during April of that year; one died in prison, three were acquitted and one was pilloried and given a prison sentence. The remaining eight were publicly

The Mace is of silver-gilt and was given to Clitheroe in 1672 by the second Duke of Albermarle and the various out-burgesses whose coats-of-arms are engraved on its shaft. It is 52" (132cm) long and is a fine example of the silversmith's art. It is borne before the Town Mayor on all ceremonial occasions

executed by hanging, probably on 20th August. Of the eight executed six had been born with some physical disfigurement. A young man, whose testimony was critical to the convictions, was the grandson of one of the executed. He was mentally unbalanced and was quickly frightened into saying anything that would please his examiners. Today the story of the Pendle witches is widely celebrated and brings many visitors to the area. The sad truth, however, is that superstition and prejudice played the major part in their committal and conviction.

Sir William Pudsey (1559-1629), Lord of Bolton by Bowland, owned the Skeleron lead mine located not far from Clitheroe and is remembered for extracting silver from the ore.

In 1671 Webster reports, "…in the reign of Queen Elizabeth [Pudsey] did there get good store of silver ore and converted it to his own use (or rather coined it as many believe, there being many florins marked with an Escalope, which the people of that Country call Pudsey's Shillings to this day)".

An early photograph of skating on the Ribble. Pye's Studio, Burnley

If Pudsey had found a high silver concentration in the ore then the mine would have been declared a 'Mine Royal' and likely have been taken from him by the Crown. An alternative explanation was that he was obtaining the silver by trimming the edges from the silver coins of the day, a widespread practice that eventually led to the milled edges still found on today's high face value coins. There is no record of any charge of counterfeiting but, whatever the truth of the matter, Pudsey was said to have escaped on horseback, jumping over a cliff at Bolton by Bowland, called Pudsey's Leap; he then rode to London and was forgiven by Queen Elizabeth I. That the Queen was his godmother may have helped his cause. More recent analyses of the ore indicate a silver content of less than 0.1kg per ton of ore compared with 12kg per ton demonstrated to Webster. The last serious attempt to work the mine finished in 1885 when the operating company went into liquidation. The presence of metalliferous ores in limestone can play havoc with

cement manufacture but fortunately there are no such deposits near the cement works.

Several notable people are associated with the area. Captain James King, friend and companion of James Cook and former pupil of Clitheroe Royal Grammar School, commanded Cook's second vessel and took full command after Cook's death on Hawaii. Arthur Conan Doyle attended Stonyhurst College, just a few miles west of Clitheroe. Although the 'Hound of the Baskervilles' is set in Dartmoor, he used local scenes for Baskerville Hall. J R R Tolkien worked on 'Lord of the Rings' during a period when he taught at Stonyhurst. Frank Whittle was a regular visitor to the town. From 1941 to 1943 the Rover Company undertook the critical early development and testing of jet engines at Waterloo Mill, barely a mile from the cement works. The noise of engine testing could be heard ten miles away.

Clitheroe, according to the old proverb, is noted for 'Law, Lime and Latin'. The 'latin' refers to the Royal Grammar School, founded in 1554, and the reason for the 'lime' should already be clear! The 'law' refers to the large number of solicitors involved in the administration of the Honour of Clitheroe, some no doubt needed to resolve disputes over lime burning. In the 18th Century the Reverend Wilson described the town as a nest of attorneys.

In the mid 1970s local government reorganisation created the Ribble Valley Borough Council. The coat of arms has at its base, a green band representing agriculture with outcrops of limestone coloured silver.

Ribble Valley Borough Council coat of arms

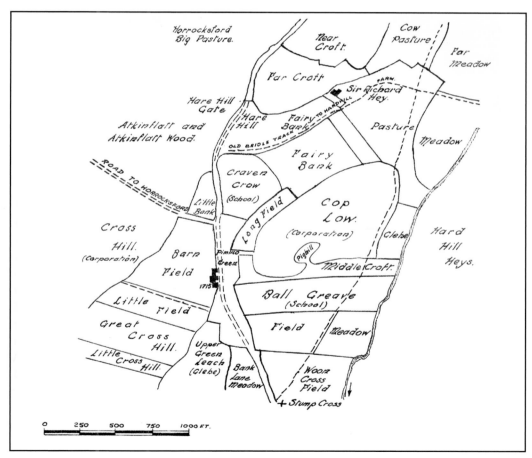

The road from Stump Cross to Little Bank is now Pimlico Road. The road from Little Bank over Hare Hill is Chatburn Old Road

Chapter 2
Limestone and lime

Limestone is a sedimentary rock consisting mainly of calcium carbonate, the fossilised remains of the hard parts of animals and algae. Limestones are being formed today in places such as the Great Barrier Reef of Australia, the Persian Gulf and even, very slowly, off the west coast of Scotland. Pure limestones, such as chalk, are white in colour but most, such as the impure limestones found around Clitheroe, are darkened by clay and by carbon, which is also organic in origin.

If limestone is heated by geological processes then the calcium carbonate re-crystallises and all traces of the fossils are obliterated. The rock then becomes marble. Both hard limestone and marble can be worked with metal tools and take a good polish, so they have been used decoratively for millennia.

Man's chief fascination with limestone has not been with its decorative properties but with what happens when it is heated. At temperatures above about 800 degrees Celsius calcium carbonate breaks down and carbon dioxide gas is given off. What remains is quick lime, calcium oxide.

The limelight

If quick lime is heated in an oxygen and hydrogen flame it glows brightly. This property was used for theatre lighting and led to the expression 'being in the limelight'.

Quick lime is hazardous and reacts violently with water. It was quick lime that was manufactured in the old lime kilns scattered about the Ribble valley.

The outcome of mixing quick lime with just sufficient water to convert it to calcium hydroxide is 'hydrated lime' or 'lime hydrate', the pale grey dry powder that can be bought from a builder's merchant. Mixed with excess water it becomes 'slaked lime', a suspension of hydrated lime. Slaked lime was mixed with sand or coal ash to make the familiar lime mortar that was the dominant material used in building from the Middle Ages to the mid 19th Century.

Lime mortar hardens because the hydrated lime within it reacts with carbon dioxide in the atmosphere and reverts

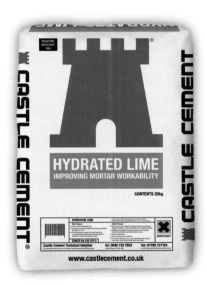

Hydrated lime, usually referred to as hydrate

to limestone. The great disadvantage of lime mortar is that it won't harden under water or in foundations, where there is no exposure to carbon dioxide.

Quick lime is an alkali and early in the sixteenth century it was discovered that agricultural productivity could be improved by spreading lime on the land. Small lime kilns were built in areas where limestone cropped out at the surface and no doubt farmers, in quiet times of the year, produced lime for their own and local commercial use. This wasn't a cheap process though, as about a ton of coal would have been required to produce a ton of lime in one of those early batch process kilns.

To cause the maximum confusion all the different forms of lime mentioned above, hazardous or not, tend to be referred to as 'lime'.

The grey powder that we call cement is quite different. Cement, water and sand are combined to make mortar, which with the addition of aggregates becomes concrete. What makes cement different from lime and what makes it such a valuable material is that it hardens not by exposure to atmospheric carbon dioxide but by a chemical reaction with water. For this reason it was once called 'hydraulic cement'. Keeping concrete permanently wet does not harm its properties in the least, so that makes it ideal for use in foundations and underwater structures.

Quarry faces and blast hole drilling machine

Chapter 3
Our heritage

A history should begin at the beginning, but when was the beginning of commercial activity on the site? We know from documentary evidence that limestone from within the area now owned by the cement works has been worked at least since the late 16th Century. At that time Fairy Bank was common land and lime burners leased working areas from the Corporation. One of the oldest Lancashire records preserved is the verdict of the Great Court or Leet of 30th October 1593; this refers to an earlier byelaw of 1587 and in stating 'Wee laye a payne that noe outmane shall burn any lyme in ffaribancke in payne of every kiln 20s' (£1) rules out lime burning other than by townspeople. A pound was a huge sum of money in those days. Pimlico, the location of Coplow quarry, is mentioned in leases of 1676 and 1681. The origin of the name Pimlico is unknown although it is clearly of some antiquity; even London's Pimlico is only documented from 1626.

Peter Parkes on Whalley Nab pack horse track 'hollow way'. Peter started as an apprentice and has worked most of his 42 years service at Ribblesdale

Last of the pack horses, died September 1902.

From the 16th to the 18th Century, lime was normally transported by pack horse. The accounts of the Shuttleworth family, later of Gawthorpe Hall, show that in 1583 'twoe fellowes of Clytherall wch came with lime' were paid 12d (5p) and in 1594 John Usherwood of Clytherowe was paid 7s 6d (37p) for 'fourtene mettes of vnsleckt lime'. Transporting slaked lime by pack horse would not have made much sense. Apart from the extra difficulty of containing a liquid, the extra weight of water would have to be carried too. It would have made much more sense to slake the lime at point of use.

(1) Bellman quarry, (2) Mediaeval strip fields, running from the Roman road at the near end to Worston in the distance. The A59 now cuts across these fields, (3) Rydal place, (4) Bold Venture, (5) Bellman lime kilns, (6) Park House, (7) Line of the link road that now passes between Coplow and the works, crossing the railway over a new bridge adjacent to the old one seen in this picture, (8) Clitheroe hospital, once the workhouse, (9) Chatburn Old Road. The kink marks the line of the parish boundary, (10) Coplow, (11) Horrocksford Lime Works – despite its name this site only produced road stone and black top, (12) Isis cement works, (13) Isis office, used as an Air Raid Precaution post during the second world war, (14) Bona Vista and Hillside, purchased by the Company for renting to employees, (15) Rail track to Cross Hill and Dangerous Quarry, (16) West Bradford Road

With thanks to the Clitheroe Advertiser for permission to reproduce this photograph, which was one of twenty aerial photographs of the area originally published in 1930

In 1773 a Clitheroe lawyer was asked, under oath, 'Is not Clitheroe one of the great marts for lime in the country?' He replied that between 500 and 1,000 pack horse loads went through Clitheroe every day. Each train of pack horses, led by a bell-horse, would walk from the lime works towards Clitheroe past Causeway House where the road was a yard wide and cobbled. Causeway House, dating from no later than 1684, is now the 'Waggon and Horses' on Pimlico Road. During the 18th Century pack horse tracks to Darwen were used for reciprocal trade in lime and coal. It is no wonder that

with such heavy usage the tracks wore down into deep cuttings, now called hollow ways. There is a fine example on Whalley Nab. The horses used were called 'lime gals', the name coming from Galloway where these sturdy ponies were bred.

Pack horses also took lime to Morecambe and returned with cockles and mussels. This is the origin of the cockle and mussel feast held in May every year in Clitheroe after the Mayor making ceremony.

Pimlico cottages and the Black Horse pub with Coplow lime works behind. The cottages were built by Giles Hoyle in 1816 for his workers

Bitumen delivery to Horrocksford

According to its letter heading, the Horrocksford Lime Company Limited (Horrocksford) was founded in 1750. Langshaw states that Atkinflatt and Atkinflatt Wood, the area now occupied by the cement works, were enclosed in the 16th Century and leased to the owners of Horrocksford on the condition that they supplied a sufficient bull to run with the cattle on Clitheroe Commons. This arrangement caused a great deal of trouble for the Corporation, who once they had realised what a shocking bargain this was, attempted to regain the land. The owners of Horrocksford stuck to the letter of the lease and in a late 19th century sale of the Horrocksford estate the condition regarding the bull was read out, although the Commons had by that time been enclosed and divided up more than a century earlier. It seems likely that the Horrocksford Lime Company's claim of being founded in 1750 is substantially true, even if there were occasional changes of ownership and short pauses in operation.

Horrocksford asphalt laying on West Bradford Road

Victoria Mill, Chatburn in the late 1960s looking towards the cement works. Taken by Sheila Haywood, landscape architect

Horrocksford Advertisement 1920s. Pye's Studio, Burnley

The millennium year passed without recognition that it was at least the 400th birthday of industrial activity on the site.

Clearly the local limestone around Clitheroe had been utilised for many hundreds of years, but the dramatic development of the textile industry in the 19th Century also brought jobs and workers to the Clitheroe area. Chatburn, Grindleton and West Bradford all developed around weaving mills. Victoria mill in Chatburn employed 500 people and Low Moor mill in Clitheroe, later purchased by Ribblesdale Cement, employed at its peak more than 700. As the 19th century progressed, however, steam powered mills in towns like Manchester superseded the old water powered mills and textile manufacture in the Ribble valley began its long decline.

Bold Venture in 1948. The remains of the old lime kilns can be seen in the foreground, in line with the cottages

Completed in 1816, the Leeds Liverpool canal was originally planned to pass to the west of Whalley and south of Clitheroe. However, in 1777 the money ran out and due to the American War of Independence no more money was available until 1790. By then coal had been discovered near Burnley and the canal was rerouted, leading to reduced mill building activity in the Ribble valley during the first half of the 19th Century. It seems, therefore, that we owe to the Americans the more rural character of the Ribble valley compared with the more industrial Calder valley to the south.

In 1824 Baines reported in his Directory and Gazetteer of Lancashire that at Pimlico there were inexhaustible supplies of limestone with ten kilns that were kept burning for forty weeks per year.

In July 1850 the railway link from Blackburn to Chatburn was first opened to light traffic and by 1851 a siding linked it to the Horrocksford Lime Company works. Rail transport stimulated a growth in limestone based job opportunities to replace those lost in textiles. From 1850 to 1865 though, there were still 24 mills in the Ribble Valley.

The population of Clitheroe increased from 1,368 in 1801 to five times that in 1851 and to 11,414 in 1901, an indication of the huge impact of textile and extractive industries on the growth of the town. By 1914, though, Clitheroe had just 13 mills containing 134,402 spindles

Rail tunnel under Bellman lime kilns showing wooden chutes for loading

Bellman lime kilns, showing the wooden bridge linking the end of the tramway with the kilns

The staff of Bold Venture Lime Company Limited

COL. J.F.M. ROBINSON.

FRANK ALLEN.
JIM SMALLEY.

WALTER SHUTTLEWORTH.
ALF ROBINSON
TOMMY NIELSON
TOMMY COUPE.
HARRY RICHARDS (JUN)
BERNARD O'NEIL
GEORGE BOYER
HARRY RICHARDS (SNR).
ARTHUR TOMLINSON
BILL MONK.
EDGAR JOHNSON

JACK RICHARDS.
TOMMY WALTON.
TOM WIGNALL
DICK DOUGLAS
ARNOLD PALMER.
BILL BENNINGTON
HARRY BLEAZARD.

JACK ADDISON
BILL EARNSHAW
GEORGE CLARK.

MISS G.C. FREEMAN.

JIM RIGBY.
CAPT JACK ROBINSON.
MR. DAWSON

Editor
London Times

ALF DEWHURST
ROBINSON
JOE DODD
ALBERT WHITEY

BILLY MASON

BILLY ROBINSON

GILBERT PARKINSON

JACK CHESTER

BILL DUNN

HOOLEY

— 27 —

BOLD VENTURE LIME WORKS.

With a view to encourage habits of sobriety and temperance, and to promote the comfort and happiness of the several persons employed at these works, and their families, I propose to give a gratuity of one week's wages, to every man and boy who shall be in my service on the 1st of November, 1849, either as Book-keeper, Quarryman, Lime-burner, Drawer, Carter, Labourer, or in any other capacity, and who shall make a solemn Declaration before a Magistrate, that he has not for the space of one year then next preceding, partaken of any Spirituous Liquor, Ale, Beer, or other intoxicating drink.

Clitheroe Castle, **21st** *October,* 1848.

This notice was put up by Mr Dixon Robinson, proprietor of Bold Venture. He was a man of strict Victorian values and a member of the Temperance Movement. He was probably horrified by the drinking of the navvies who were working on the railway line in the late 1840s. In 1821 he became a partner with Thomas Carr, solicitor and steward of the Honour of Clitheroe. In 1836, on Carr's death, he took over his position. Robinson's home and offices were at Clitheroe Castle until his own death in 1878

Bold Venture lime works in Chatburn was operating small limekilns in 1780. The Company was bought by Dixon Robinson, a Clitheroe solicitor, in 1827. Included in the contract for the quarry and two kilns were 36 lime gals. The kilns were greatly enlarged in 1860 to give work to the unemployed at the time of the cotton famine. At the same time Robinson installed gas retorts so that the people of Chatburn would benefit from a gas supply for lighting. By the time Clitheroe Corporation installed a public gas supply in 1927, ten retorts were in operation and the gas was stored in a 9,000 cubic feet gasometer. The gas retorts were operated for almost fifty years by Thomas Wignall. When Wignall retired after 58 years service he reported that gas had been 7s (35p) per thousand cubic feet when he started and was the same price when he finished.

The inscription reads 'This fountain was erected by the workpeople at Salt Hill and Bellman quarries in memory of their late employer James Carter, who worked amongst us from 1869 to 1903.' The picture was taken in the early 1990s. Since then the memorial has been conserved and has been repositioned not far from its original location

and 8,463 looms. Mill closures peaked in the early 30's and mid 50's and today only one specialist operation remains.

Manchester was the world's first industrial city and the birthplace of the factory system of manufacture. Its population grew from a mere 20,000 in 1771 to over 700,000 in 1919. In 1926 over three million bales of raw cotton were unloaded at Liverpool and almost 600,000 people in the Manchester Liverpool conurbation were employed in scores of textile factories. The textile-based industrial revolution had fuelled demand for building materials, lime for mortar from Derbyshire and the Ribble Valley and fuel from the Manchester and Burnley coalfields. The opening of the railway connection to Clitheroe in 1850 galvanised entrepreneurs into action, for in the Ribble Valley they found the nearest good outcrops of limestone north of Manchester.

Coplow lime works mainly operated post 1850. A lease from Clitheroe Corporation in 1851 required the stone to be 'got and worked in a good and workmanlike manner' and that 'the soil off the rock be laid sideways and afterwards spread where the rock has been got up so as to cover the surface and convert it into pasture land'. This must be a very early example of a requirement for quarry restoration. A standard gauge mineral railway connected Coplow by bridge over Pimlico Road. Rockmount, the house adjacent to the quarry entrance, used to be the home of Henry Parkinson. Henry Parkinson was an extraordinary man. He trained as a plasterer but work was so short in Clitheroe that he set off to walk to Lancaster with only two 'sad cakes' and a few coppers. On his way he met a man in more need than himself and gave away the coppers. In Lancaster he prospered and on his return to Clitheroe he set up in business as a master builder, building such local landmarks as Byrne's

premises in King Street, a row of houses in York Street and cottages in Chatburn Road. It was Henry Parkinson who purchased Horrocksford, then not in operation, modernised it and restored it to health. Coplow lime works was also run by him, literally in his back yard, and he also founded the Waddington brick and tile works. Later he became Alderman Parkinson and was a member of the Limestone Rock Lodge of the Freemasons.

From 1868 to 1874 considerable interest was aroused in Clitheroe and surrounding villages when a series of huge blasts, three at Coplow and two at Salthill, were witnessed by thousands of people. The boring for the first blast was carried out by fourteen experienced miners from Holywell, north Wales. A blast hole would have been excavated into the face in the form of a T with explosives placed at the extremities. On one occasion seventy barrels of powder were used and the weight of

Ruston Bucyrus RB54 excavator

rock displaced was said to be 140,000 tons, about three times as much as would be normal today. The shock was felt throughout Clitheroe and even as far as Low Moor. A Preston paper reported an earthquake in Low Moor, but this was from another small blast in nearby Dangerous quarry. Zadkiel, in his almanac, had predicted earthquakes in England at this time, and in the almanac for the following year claimed fulfilment of his prophesy.

Bellmanpark Lime Works was opened in about 1869 by James Carter and William Rowe. In 1877 limekilns were erected on a siding adjacent to the main railway line. A tramway, incorporating an endless chain, connected Bellman quarry to the kilns. Stone wagons were pulled by horse to the quarry end of the chain, weighed and attached to the chain. The returning strand brought the empties back. The opening scene of 'Whistle Down the Wind', filmed in about 1961, shows the children rescuing three kittens by the tramway. The lime was loaded

Dumper tipping into Horrocksford crushing plant

Limmer and Trinidad Workforce, left to right: E Stinson, J Skirrow, R Crompton, T Rose, H Boyer, A Driver, C Boyer, A Crook, R Kay, M Bridge, T Boyer, A Dixon, F Wilson, W Dixon, M Waddington, K Chamley, L Ridgeway, B Bartlett, D Pinch, E Smales, B McVarish, J Marsden, H Wallbank, J Conchie, R Dewhurst, J Ainsworth, J Abraham, D Marsden, B Boyer, J Ingham, M Ingham, C Snape, G Zejer, J Winterbottom, R Ashton, D Wilson, H Whaites, J Attard, H Chatburn

directly from the kilns into railway wagons. Behind the limekilns a further siding ran to a 25 ton per week cement shaft kiln built between the Chatburn road and the main line. The Carter Rowe partnership was dissolved in 1879, but James Carter and Sons worked Bellman and Salthill until 1959/60 and the cement kiln was operated by William Rowe from 1879 until his death in 1889.

Peach quarry, a bank of four limekilns just south of Chatburn road and opposite the Chatburn trading estate, also operated in the last half of the 19th century and perhaps earlier.

Working horse, possibly from Bellman quarry

Limmer and Trinidad Asphalt (1) raw asphalt melting, (2) asphalt mixing with additives, (3) rock store, (4) finished asphalt cooling, (5) finished product store. Buildings 3, 4 and 5 are now spare parts stores. The remainder, plus the buildings on the opposite side of the railway by the West Bradford Road entrance, have been demolished

Isis cement works, with six shaft kilns, was established on 3 acres of land leased in 1893, from the Horrocksford Lime Company, for 60 years at a cost of £60 10s per annum. The lessee was required to provide suitable plant and machinery and to purchase all stone and clay from the Horrocksford Lime Company to the value of at least £200 per annum. In 1911 Isis erected a windmill to pump water out of the clay pits. The Clitheroe newspaper clearly thought that it added something to the view and described it as both useful and picturesque.

Clitheroe Asphalt works, established during the 1920's by Penmaenmawr and Trinidad Lake Asphalt Company Ltd, was situated on the north side of the works railway line just east of West Bradford Road. It produced mastic asphalt for roofing, roads and waterproofing, using ground limestone from the Horrocksford works in the production process. Later it became Limmer and

Demolition of Isis. One bottle kiln and the stack remains.
On the far side of the railway track is the Horrocksford works

1939 Isis stack finally demolished

Trinidad and their black and yellow trucks were a familiar sight in the area. The operation was purchased by Tarmac in 1972 and closed.

Horrocksford Lime works, sited close to the present cement works 'wigwam' clinker store, had 43 operatives in 1851.

The history of the site is summarised below:-

1587/1593	Byelaws re lime burning. These suggest that lime burning in the area was already on an industrial scale
1750	Founding of the business that became Horrocksford Lime
1825/27	Chatburn New Road, a turnpike road, opened
1837	Bold Venture lime works purchased by Dixon Robinson
1870s	Start of cement manufacture on the Bellman lime kilns site near to Chatburn New Road
1870-74	Horrocksford Lime works operated by William Briggs
1874	Clitheroe Lime Company Ltd formed
1890	Clitheroe Lime Company wound up
1892	Henry Parkinson reopened Horrocksford works
1895	Isis Portland Cement Company started operation
1898	Carter completed a rail link from Salthill to the lime kilns at Bellman via Park Hill tunnel under Chatburn New Road. 25,000 tons of spoil were moved during construction, mostly by horse
1899	Horrocksford Lime Company leased Coplow quarry
1924	Opening of major extension at Bold Venture
1929	Isis ceased operation
1935	Present cement works site purchased by Ribblesdale Cement Ltd and construction of the new cement works commenced
1939	Isis cement works chimney stack demolished

In 1982 RTZ Cement was formed through the acquisition of Tunnel Cement, Ketton Cement and Ribblesdale Cement. The new, combined company was renamed Castle Cement in 1986 and in 1988 was purchased by Scancem, a joint venture between two Scandinavian public companies, Aker AS of Norway and Euroc AB of Sweden. In 1995 Euroc merged with Aker's cement and building materials division to form Scancem AB. In 1999 Scancem AB was bought by HeidelbergCement, the current owner of the site.

Chapter 4
The history of cement
and how it is made

The Romans invented cement. Chemically their cement wasn't quite the same as today's but it was a close relative. The main difference is that modern cements achieve most of their high strength in about a week whereas Roman cements were less strong and would have taken many weeks to achieve their full strength. The emperor Hadrian rebuilt the Pantheon, a great temple to all the gods of the pagan world. It has a free standing concrete dome 43.5 metres in diameter. To keep the weight down pumice was used as an aggregate. The dome was cast on wooden shuttering so this magnificent building demonstrates both an early use of light weight aggregates and of cast in situ concrete.

After the fall of the Roman empire the techniques for the manufacture and use of cement were forgotten, so mediaeval masons built huge Romanesque and Gothic cathedrals with lime mortar as a binder. Lime mortar does not harden and gain strength unless exposed to air, this is why so many of these great buildings have required remedial work on their foundations. The commercial opportunity for anyone who could re-invent cement was clear for all to see.

Pantheon

Pantheon

The Eddystone Lighthouse. Christopher Nicholson, Alamy

One of the first great pioneers was John Smeaton (1724-1792), a lawyer's son, who trained as an instrument maker and later became a surveyor and an engineer. In preparation for rebuilding the Eddystone lighthouse in 1756-59 he carried out a series of systematic experiments with raw materials from various locations across the country. As the base of the lighthouse was at sea level he was trying to find a variety of lime that would set in permanently wet conditions. He succeeded in making a near relative of modern cement, now called hydraulic lime. This sets and hardens under water but attains its strength much more slowly than modern cements. Roman cement was really hydraulic lime.

In 1796 James Parker of Northfleet in Kent took out a patent for a "certain Cement or Tarras" and later publicised a product which he called 'Roman cement'. For raw materials, he and his competitors used nodules of limestone and chalk from the beaches of the Thames estuary. It is likely that he too made hydraulic lime.

In France the academic Louis Joseph Vicat (1786-1861) conducted scientific tests on limes and limestones. He worked from 1812, through the last years of the emperor Napoleon, to 1818, under the regime of the restored king, Louis XVII. According to Captain J T Smith (1805-82) of the Royal Engineers, who brought out translations in 1837, Vicat's publications of 1818 and 1828 marked a

Isis cement works circa 1930, about a year after it closed

"practical and scientific" approach to calcareous mortars and cements, combined with a "theoretical investigation of their properties and modes of action".

In contrast, it was a Yorkshire bricklayer, Joseph Aspdin (1778-1855), who coined the name of our modern cement when he took out a patent in 1824. It is not clear whether his 'Portland Cement', said to be burnt at 1,100-1,300°C, was anything more than a marketing stratagem. The claimed temperature is critical as hydraulic lime can be made at temperatures not much above 900°C whereas true modern cement requires temperatures in excess of 1,400°C. It would have been extremely difficult for Joseph to achieve such high temperatures consistently with the kiln technology of that time. The word Portland comes from the supposed resemblance of Aspdin's concrete to the highly regarded Portland stone from Dorset.

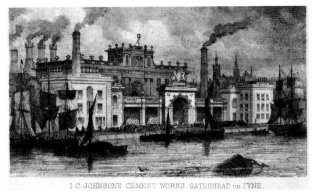

I C Johnson factory at Gateshead.
Picture courtesy of Central Library, Gateshead

Early kiln, said to have been used by Robins, Aspdin & Co.

Joseph's son, William Aspdin, claimed that the great engineer Isambard Kingdom Brunel had used his father's cement to plug a great leak in his tunnel under the Thames, a claim which seems to have been quite untrue as Brunel himself noted that he filled the leak with sacks of clay with hazel-rods stuck through to hold them together.

Despite this, William Aspdin was manufacturing something approaching a modern Portland cement at Northfleet in Kent by the 1850s. It was first used in 1858-75 on a very large scale by J W Bazalgette (1819-91), chief engineer to the Metropolitan Board of Works, for the main drainage system of London. He designed the Embankments along the Thames, primarily to cover his main collecting sewers, but in places covering an underground railway there too. He was knighted in 1874 for the skill and vigour with which he carried through this project, so vital for public health.

I C Johnson (1811-1911), manager of a cement works at Northfleet near that of the younger Aspdin's, set up his own works at Frindsbury near Rochester in 1851. He later claimed to be the inventor of Portland cement and certainly, through many experiments, played some part in its development.

All the early cements were made using shaft kilns, a technology still used today in some parts of the world. The modern method of manufacturing cement, using slightly inclined rotating tubular kilns, is just over a century old. In 1900 six rotary kilns were installed in a works in West Thurrock, Essex; this works was part of the group that eventually became Castle Cement.

Cement and its manufacture have scarcely featured in art and literature. However, in the 1920s William Heath Robinson (1872-1944), the celebrated cartoonist known for his weirdly logical but very unlikely-looking machinery, was commissioned by G & T Earle of Wilmington to make a series of humorous drawings on the making of cement.

Like bread, made for millennia without any deep understanding of chemistry, cement is made to a recipe. Different flours and production techniques result in different colours and styles of bread, but all clearly recognisable as bread. In the same way different limestone and clay raw materials produce cements of different colours and properties, all clearly recognisable as cement and all setting by chemical reaction with water. Like bread also, the cement recipe was developed by trial and error.

Heath Robinson (1872-1944). Picture by kind permission of Lafarge UK

QUARRYING

Heath Robinson (1872-1944). Picture by kind permission of Lafarge UK

Clinker store with kiln 7 preheater tower in the background, taken post 2002

The traditional recipe for cement is 80% limestone and 20% clay and sand. At Ribblesdale much of the limestone is not very pure and already contains almost sufficient clay. On old geological maps these impure limestones were sometimes called cement stones.

In order to meet modern quality requirements the recipe at Ribblesdale is approximately 85% limestone, 5% sandstone and 10% fly ash, the ash residue from burning coal in power stations.

The remainder of this chapter explains the cement making process in a little more detail.

The process of manufacture consists of four stages, the preparation of raw meal, which is the ground up raw material, the cooking of the raw meal in a kiln to a temperature of about 1,400°C to make clinker, the cooling of the clinker and the grinding of clinker with about 5% gypsum to make the familiar grey powder, cement.

Raw meal has to be of the correct recipe and has to be ground finely. The chemical reactions in the kiln will not take place quickly enough if the raw meal is too coarse. Typically all the raw meal particles must pass through a sieve having holes 1/10 millimetre diameter.

At Ribblesdale the technology for raw meal preparation on kilns 1 to 6 was the 'wet process', so called because the raw meal was ground with minimal water into slurry. Slurries are easy to handle and homogenise but all of the water has to be boiled away in the kiln so the heat consumption is high. In kiln 6, which produced 1,000 tons per day of clinker, more than 500 tons per day of water had to be evaporated. Kiln 7 uses dry process technology where hot exhaust gas from the kiln passes through the grinding mill to produce dry raw meal to feed to the kiln system.

In the kiln system two main chemical reactions take place, calcination, which drives off carbon dioxide from the limestone component, and clinkering which is the final reaction during which the material forms near spherical black nodules up to 50mm in diameter. Kiln 7 is properly called a precalciner kiln because the raw meal is both heated and calcined before it enters the rotary kiln. When kiln 7 was commissioned in 1983, it was the first precalciner kiln in the UK. The technology has not changed much; today's precalciner kilns are very similar.

Heath Robinson (1872-1944). Picture by kind permission of Lafarge UK

F L Smidth engineer checking the internals of a large cement mill

The clinker is air cooled. Heat is transferred from clinker to air and the hot air produced is used for combustion of the fuel. This heat recovery saves energy.

Finally, when cool, the clinker is ground in ball mills with about 5% gypsum to make OPC, Ordinary Portland Cement. Many grades of cement are now made with minor additional components added to achieve the specific properties required by the customer.

David Grooby conducting routine maintenance in a slurry mill

Cement mills 9, 10 and 11

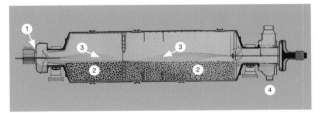

Cross section of a typical cement mill.

(1) clinker and gypsum input
(2) grinding media consisting of hardened steel balls
(3) water sprays used for cooling
(4) cement out
The mill rotates at about 16 revolutions per minute

Kiln 6, 164 metres long. (1) section of kiln for slurry drying; this is the section with chains hanging inside, (2) calcining zone, (3) clinkering or burning zone, (4) planetary coolers

The process used in the shaft kilns by Isis cement from 1895 to 1929 was similar and was described by the manager, Charles Spackman, and his son in a visit report of 2nd August 1912 in the Clitheroe Advertiser. The finely ground raw meal was prepared dry and then enough water was added to make briquettes. Briquettes of raw meal and lump coke were fed to the top of the cylindrical 'shaft' kiln in alternate layers. Clinker was regularly removed from the base of the kiln and fresh briquettes and coke were added to the top so that a continuous process was maintained. Combustion took place inside the kiln using preheated fresh air that had passed up through the base of the kiln, cooling the clinker en route. Temperatures in excess of 1,000°C would have been achieved in the hottest part of the kiln and the briquettes of raw meal converted to clinker. After combustion the hot waste gas then passed through the recently added briquettes and coke to preheat them. There was no dust

collection, but a chimney was required to improve the draught through the kiln; with increased air flow more combustion could take place and the output would be greater. It was very important that fuel and raw material remained as coarse particles, otherwise the flow of air for combustion through the kiln would be impeded and the fire would die down and eventually be extinguished. Poke holes were provided near the base of the kiln to break up large lumps of fused briquettes. The similarity of these lumps to the clinker arising from a coal fire may have been the reason for the word clinker being adopted in cement manufacture.

Charles Spackman (1848-1932) was a pioneer cement maker and cement chemist. He worked on the construction of Alexandra Palace and in 1873, on the occasion of the great fire, narrowly escaped with his life. He designed and built cement kilns in Leicestershire and did similar work in Ireland before coming to Clitheroe

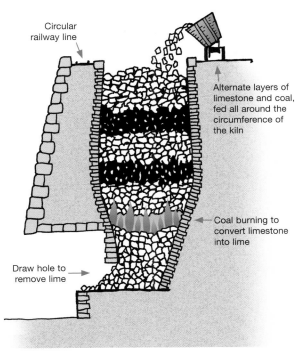

Circular railway line

Alternate layers of limestone and coal, fed all around the circumference of the kiln

Coal burning to convert limestone into lime

Draw hole to remove lime

Limekiln – diagram of a continuous process shaft kiln, also called a draw kiln

Kiln 7

(1) preheater tower containing 4 cylcone stages
(2) calciner inside preheater at this level
(3) kiln, 58 metres long
(4) cooler
(5) exhaust gas scrubber

as managing director of the Isis works. He was a fellow of the Chemical Society of London and in 1905 co-wrote with Gilbert Redgrave 'Calcareous cements: their nature, manufacture and uses', a standard work that ran to three editions. Magnesite refractory bricks, used in steel making, were imported from Germany, so following the outbreak of the first world war the government asked Spackman to devise a method of manufacture. Fortunately he had learnt German a few years earlier and with data extracted from some German technical papers and extensive experiments carried out at the Isis works he was able to find a solution. So successful was he that his services were offered to the French Ministry of Munitions. He was a quiet man, who avoided publicity, but he was widely read and as interested in the arts as in the sciences. On his death his personal library contained some 4,000 volumes.

The cost of production at Isis was 25s (£1.25) per ton in 1925 and about 15,000 tons per annum were produced.

In the mid 1930s some unused raw meal briquettes from the abandoned works were analysed; that recipe had a lime saturation factor of 103 and a silica modulus of 2.6, both very close to today's targets and certainly good enough to make perfectly adequate cement clinker.

The shaft kiln process used by Isis and other early manufacturers to make clinker is closely analogous to that of lime manufacture; just replace the raw meal briquettes with lumps of limestone and the coke with coal and you have a lime shaft kiln.

Chapter 5
Ribblesdale Cement Works – from its beginnings to 1950

In about 1930 H B Milne from consulting engineers Parry and Elmquist came to assess Isis cement works. He is remembered as a self-effacing and very conscientious man. Many years later his son John supervised civil work on the site. Milne concluded that it would not be economic to develop Isis. A little later Ketton's George Thompson came to investigate the limestone reserves and took samples back to Ketton for analysis. In 1934

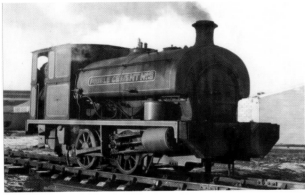

Hudswell Clarke saddle tank locomotive number 1661, delivered in May 1936. When no longer required the loco was sent to Preston for scrap. The scrap merchant thought that it looked a good engine and contacted Jim Morris, of Helical Technology, who agreed to purchase it in exchange for the same weight of steel scrap. Jim put coal in it, fired it up and it ran beautifully. The engine, very smartly repainted, remains in his possession

Left: Winterbottom, father of Joe; centre: Donald Brewer, father of Alan who was a driver from 1965-97; 2nd from right: Teddy Punchard

Construction, top right John King, steam crane in background

Parry and Elmquist reported positively to the Ketton Board on the prospects at Clitheroe, with the caveat that under the new Cement Makers' Federation rules the Ketton Cement Company would be considered as owner and that the quota allotted to Ketton would have to be shared with Ribblesdale.

Erection of cement mill 1 including Donald Brewer (2nd left); Teddy Punchard, father of Terry (3rd left) and Thurston Haslam (2nd right)

Two existing cement companies, then known as Tunnel Portland Cement Company Ltd (Tunnel) and Ketton Portland Cement Company Ltd (Ketton), controlled by Thomas W Ward, were keen to establish a new cement works in the area.

They decided to work together rather than compete so the appropriately named Ribblesdale Cement Ltd (Ribble), a private limited company with a planned capitalisation of £600,000, was created to build a two kiln plant. Parry and Elmquist Ltd of Scunthorpe were Consulting Engineers and F L Smidth Ltd machinery suppliers.

Clitheroe Council was very supportive of the project because unemployment in the area was so high. At this time the textile industry was in a recession from which it never recovered. Alderman Boothman went to Sheffield to meet Joseph Ward to encourage him to go ahead with the new works; both men were Wesleyan Methodists. During the mayoral visit to the cement works in 1937 Joseph Ward paid a special tribute to

Teddy Punchard and Eddie Hunt in 1935

Thomas W Ward started as a coal merchant. In the great war his dray horses were requisitioned. Ever the entrepreneur, Ward used an elephant called 'Lizzie'. The elephant was a familiar sight around Sheffield. Picture from the collections in Sheffield Local Studies Library, reproduced with permission

all that Alderman Boothman had done to overcome the numerous difficulties that beset the founding of the new cement works.

Each parent company provided a joint managing director and had equal representation on the Board. In addition Joseph Ward of Thomas W Ward Ltd Sheffield (Wards), effectively the owners of Ketton, became Chairman.

Tunnel was part owned by F L Smidth and with former Smidth engineers in important positions it could be said to be stronger technically than Wards. Their joint managing director was N M (Max) Jenson a formidable figure in the cement industry. His eventual successor was Carl Hagerup, a Norwegian who was more hands-on at Ribblesdale. On one of his visits he revealed that he had once managed a cement works in Egypt with 2,000 employees.

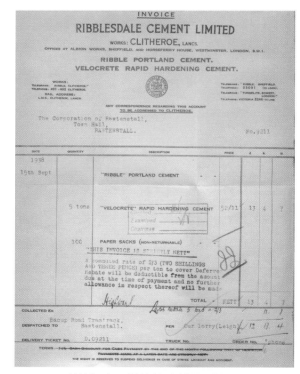

1938 invoice of £12.13s 4d (£12.67) for 5 tons of rapid hardening cement delivered in 1cwt paper sacks

Wards had Joseph Ward as chairman. He was a staunch teetotaller so alcoholic drinks were kept out of his sight when he visited the works office. On a visit to the works, during its construction, he collapsed and later sent five shillings to every man who had come to his assistance.

Representing Wards as the other joint managing director was F R Stagg who was probably more familiar with the steel construction industry. He was succeeded by his son, Rawson F Stagg, who was more approachable and made many visits to Ribblesdale.

It was Joseph Ward who asked J H Billson to become manager at Ribblesdale, no doubt impressed by his achievements at Ketton.

The administration of Ribble was largely in the hands of Wards and they provided a succession of company secretaries over the years. Although a copy of every order for the purchase of goods was sent to each parent company, it was Wards who kept the closest eye on things, insisting that everything that the Ward Group could supply should be bought from them. When Wards set up its pension fund under the name of Forward Pensions Securities Limited in 1948, the staff of Ribble and Horrocksford were invited to participate. From modest beginnings it developed into an excellent pension fund.

Ruston Bucyrus electric excavator,
also known as a 'navvie', loading from quarry face

Horrocksford Hall farm dovecote, thought to date from the 16th century

Light up of kiln 2 – September 1937, photograph including Norman Niven (future kiln burner then assistant kiln foreman), J Wilson, W Ellse (cashier), J H Billson, L G Kent, E Scherman (Parry & Elmquist)

On the first three production units, built in 1936, 1937 and 1951, Wards supplied and erected all structural steelwork and installed the rail tracks. They also supplied many other items of plant, not forgetting the impressive staircase in the main office.

Reflecting the tension between the joint owners, the Ribble board appointed two supervisors to oversee the running of the works, E Elmquist on behalf of Wards and Schmit Jensen of Tunnel. The former was the head of consulting engineers Parry and Elmquist and the latter was in a management position in Tunnel. Schmit Jensen was a world expert and international judge of Arabian horses.

Horrocksford Hall Farm, purchased from Eastham Estates, comprised land bordering West Bradford road and the River Ribble. The tenant W Crook with his son Bernard had been there since the 1914-18 war and their descendants John and Kathy are still at the farm. To the east lay Horrocksford's Lanehead quarry and to the north Higher and Lower Kempstone Farms, which were acquired later.

There had been a nine-hole golf course on the land but Eastham Estates gave the club notice to quit by 1932, so they moved to Barrow Gardens where they now have an eighteen-hole course and a thriving club. They left behind a wooden club house that Ken Hogg, a loco

Edward Pye driving from the first tee at Horrocksford in 1926.
Pye's Studio, Burnley

Club House of the Horrocksford Golf Club 1934, home of Ken Hogg

driver, crane driver and future quarry fitter, occupied with his wife. The club house was in the area where 13 and 14 cement silos now stand. Mrs Hogg was from a family of confectioners and sold confectionery and sweets to the workmen from her front room. The first tee was close to a pond. Years later, when the pond was drained and the clay dug for raw material, over a thousand old golf balls came to light with names such as Pluto, Chemico Bob and Plus Colonel.

The potential market for cement was confirmed by an early order for many thousands of tons for an ordnance factory at Euxton, near Chorley. This is where the dam buster 'bouncing bombs' were filled with explosives. Instead of explosives the test bombs were filled with Ribblesdale cement to make the bombs up to the correct weight.

The capitalisation according to the accounts of 31st August 1936 was £332,000, of which £110,000 was for plant and machinery.

The chimneys for kilns 1 and 2 were each 201ft (61m) high. They were built by Tilemans, as were the two larger chimneys, at a cost of £2,000 each. On completion number 1 chimney displayed RIBBLE CEMENT in large bold black lettering vertically on the four quarters. No permission had been given for this advertisement, so not surprisingly objections were raised and the lettering had to be obscured by over-painting.

John King, aged 19, was working near the top of the new chimney when he coughed and his dentures fell to the ground. Due at a dance that evening, he recovered the three pieces and set off to the dentist with a request for an urgent fix, as he was courting Kathleen at the time. In exchange for a promise to buy a new set from the dentist the broken pieces were stuck together, clearly an important moment for John and Kathleen who later married and lived happily ever after. Their son Alan worked for maintenance and son-in-law Paul Dewhurst worked in the quarry until quite recently.

John Herbert Billson was the first works manager. He lived at Rockmount on Pimlico Road. Rockmount, backing onto the old Coplow lime works, had previously

Construction of kiln 1 with Donald Brewer on the right. Note the hand made ladder and by today's standards the lack of normal safety equipment such as hard hats, wearing of which became compulsory in 1981

All requirements for the works were in plentiful supply, limestone, water, coal, electricity, cheap labour and good access to road and rail. Water came from the Ribble and electricity from the Lancashire Electrical Power Company at Padiham. This was in contrast to Ketton where initially the power had to be generated on site. Domestic consumers in Clitheroe, who had had electrical power from 1927, paid 0.5d per kWh (about 0.2p). Longbottom Ltd, a Wards' company, supplied coal at about 14s per ton (70p) to the works from both the Lancashire and Yorkshire coalfields via the railway. Gypsum was also delivered by rail. Only later was local coal used from Hapton pit in the Burnley coalfield.

Ribble table tennis team win the league; left to right, Dennis Punchard (blacksmith), Mary Leigh, David Slinger, Terry Punchard and Donald Parker. Mary Leigh was Robin Parkinson's secretary and had previously worked, from 1942-1947, in a test cell on the Whittle gas turbine development project at Waterloo Mill

been the home of Henry Parkinson, the former owner of Horrocksford.

Betty Trueman, daughter of Robert Young Parkinson (known as Robin) and great granddaughter of Henry, remembers Joseph Ward staying at Rockmount at the time the deal for the sale of Horrocksford was being discussed. Joseph became ill and Betty's mother, Lyn, nursed him back to health. Joseph had a very full beard and was treated with such deference that, as a very small girl, Betty thought he was Jesus Christ.

One day, in a moment of youthful over-exuberance, two lads from the cement works took Billson's car for a joy ride. Their journey ended abruptly, in a ditch. On returning to the works they would not have been surprised to find that their employment had been terminated just as abruptly.

Chimney stack 1936 with unapproved 'Ribble Cement' written on the four quarters

Kiln 1 construction; much was done by hand but a steam, rail mounted, crane was also used

The office, originally consisting of the present centre section with wings of only a single storey, was built using blocks faced with Ketton freestone. The blocks were made by Jim Parker and Les Baker's father, Sid, in workshops that were originally part of the Isis works. In accordance with Wards' time honoured tradition the internals were second hand, reclaimed from shipbreaking. The staircase came from the steam ship Olympic, a sister ship to the Titanic. All the offices had posh pedestal tables covered in green leather, edged with gold lines. There were also many substantial chairs with similar green leather. The gentlemen's toilet even had grab rails for use in heavy seas. These office fittings, almost certainly from the Olympic too, were in daily use

Olympic staircase. Photographs reproduced by permission of English Heritage. NMR

*Main office staircase ex SS Olympic.
Photograph by Stuart Lythgoe*

Bernard Chatburn with Olympic 'engineers smoke room' cupboard

until the 1960s when they were thrown out in an office reorganisation. Efforts to find the present homes of this furniture have largely been in vain, but if anyone has the good fortune to possess a piece, they can consider themselves fortunate because such items are keenly sought after by collectors. One small cupboard, once in the time office at Horrocksford's Bold Venture site, has come to light. It is labelled 'Engrs. Smoke Rm, SS Olympic' on the undersides of the drawers.

Unemployment in Clitheroe was very high and some men had been out of work for six years. On Billson's journey to work from Rockmount along West Bradford Road he would regularly pass long queues of men seeking work. George Thompson, general foreman, who stayed for some time at the Black Horse, was woken every morning by the clatter of clogs as the men passed by. Men were employed on a daily basis as needed and some were so desperate that they would jump out of the queue offering to work for lower wages. Clogs, made from alder with leather uppers, were the normal footwear for working men. Foremen like George wore normal shoes, a suit and a smock.

Face loading in the late 1930s. In the foreground Horrocksford employees are hand breaking stone and loading it by hand into narrow gauge 'Jubilee' wagons. In the background an electric excavator is loading into standard gauge trucks for the cement works

RIBBLESDALE CEMENT LIMITED,

Albion Works,

SHEFFIELD.

DIRECTORS' REPORT

AND

BALANCE SHEET,

31st August, 1936.

Notice is hereby given TO THE ORDINARY SHARE-HOLDERS of the Company, that the FIRST ORDINARY GENERAL MEETING will be held at the REGISTERED OFFICE of the COMPANY, ALBION WORKS, SAVILE STREET, SHEFFIELD, on TUESDAY, 29th DECEMBER, 1936, at 2.30 p.m., to receive and consider the Report of the Directors and Auditors, and Statement of Accounts; to elect a Director, to appoint Auditors, and to transact any other ordinary business of the Company.

By Order of the Board.

H. BERESFORD,

SECRETARY.

19th DECEMBER, 1936.

LOXLEY BROS., LTD., SHEFFIELD.

Notice of first AGM 1936

Kiln 1

4.36

RIBBLESDALE CEMENT LIMITED.

Balance Sheet, as at 31st August, 1936.

	£ s. d.	£ s. d.		£ s. d.	£ s. d.
SHARE CAPITAL. Authorised and Issued.			FREEHOLD LAND, BUILDINGS, SIDINGS AND ROADS. Expenditure to 31st August, 1936, at cost		75,815 5 3
150,000 Ordinary Shares of £1 each, fully paid		150,000 0 0	CEMENT MAKING MACHINERY, PLANT AND EQUIPMENT. Expenditure to 31st August, 1936, at cost		109,842 16 7
4% Guaranteed Debenture Stock	150,000 0 0		ROLLING STOCK. Expenditure to 31st August, 1936, at cost		17,956 0 11
Add :—Interest accrued to date (gross)	1,000 0 0	151,000 0 0	PREPARATORY WORK ON ESTATE, ENGINEERS' FEES AND EXPENSES DURING CONSTRUCTION. Expenditure to 31st August, 1936, at cost		17,829 12 2
Sundry Creditors and Provision for Accrued charges and Income Tax		30,631 14 1	STOCK IN TRADE (as valued by Managing Directors)		412 15 4
Amount owing to Subsidiary Company		568 1 10	Investment in Subsidiary Company, at cost	92,203 14 0	
PROFIT AND LOSS ACCOUNT—			Add :—Profit as shown by Accounts—Eight months to 31st August, 1936	4,384 6 3	
Balance as per annexed Account		83 2 11			96,588 0 3
			Sundry Debtors and Prepayments		319 17 11
			Cash at Bank	8,688 1 11	
			Cash in Hand	14 4 7	
					8,702 6 6
			Preliminary Expenses	1,312 12 6	
			Debenture Stock Issue Expenses	2,753 11 5	
				£ s. d.	
			Commission on Issue of Debenture Stock	2,250 0 0	
			Less :—Premium received on Issue	1,500 0 0	
				750 0 0	
					4,816 3 11
		£332,282 18 10			£332,282 18 10

JOS. WARD } DIRECTORS.
N. M. JENSEN }

Profit and Loss Account for the period 13th May, 1935, to 31st August, 1936.

	£ s. d.		£ s. d.
To Balance, being Loss on Trading after charging Expenses to date, but before charging Depreciation	1,429 15 6	By Bank and other Interest	2,884 1 8
„ Debenture Stock Interest (gross)	5,421 13 4	„ Rents Receivable	149 10 6
„ Fees to Trustees for Debenture Holders	116 13 4	„ Profit as shewn by the Accounts of Subsidiary Company for the eight months to 31st August, 1936	4,384 6 3
„ Directors' Fees	366 13 4		
„ Balance transferred to Balance Sheet	83 2 11		
	£7,417 18 5		£7,417 18 5

Report of the Auditors to the Members of Ribblesdale Cement Limited.

We Report to the Members that we have examined the above Balance Sheet with the Books of the Company and have obtained all the information and explanations we have required. We are of opinion that such Balance Sheet is properly drawn up so as to exhibit a true and correct view of the state of the Company's affairs as at 31st August, 1936, according to the best of our information and the explanations given to us, and as shewn by the books of the Company.

Statement pursuant to Section 126 of the Companies Act, 1929.

The profits of the Subsidiary Company for the eight months to 31st August, 1936, have been incorporated in the above Accounts.

JOS. WARD } DIRECTORS.
N. M. JENSEN }

Balance sheet 1936

H B Milne took on the labour to build the first kilns. Pay was 1s per hour, £3.00 for a 60 hour week, and up to about 300 men were employed. One morning, as Milne walked down the queue, he came upon a man wearing rather dirty overalls and looking as though he was used to work. The man was taken on. So began the career of William (Bill) Sharples, who became packing plant foreman and eventually Mayor of Clitheroe.

Fred Braithwaite joined the team in March 1937, only a few months after kiln 1 produced its first clinker. Samuel Bowyer had taken over responsibility for building kiln 2 and Fred worked for him. Fred was soon called away to war, but on 24th July 1945 the Company applied for the early release from HM forces of Fred and a few other employees as their special experience was required for the post war building programme. It was March 1946 before Fred's release was officially confirmed.

No. 18   1946.   **MONTHLY TROUT 5/-**

SALMON AND FRESHWATER FISHERIES ACT, 1923.
RIBBLE FISHERIES PROVISIONAL ORDERS, 1913.

RIBBLE FISHERY DISTRICT.

LICENCE TO FISH FOR TROUT

(Excluding Migratory Trout)

P. J. Fehrenbach of Bona Vista   Horrocks Ford Clitheroe

in the County of Lancashire   is hereby licensed to Fish for Trout *(excluding Migratory Trout) with one Rod and Line at the times and in the places at which he is otherwise entitled so to fish within the Ribble Fishery District during one calendar month only from day of issue.*

Dated this 27d day of Aug. 1946.

A. T. R. HOUGHTON, *Clerk,*
15 Winckley Street, Preston.

This Licence covers only the person to whom it is granted.

The Licensee Fishing in pursuance of this Licence is bound under a penalty to produce it when called upon by any Licensee under the Salmon and Fresh-water Fisheries Act, 1923, who produces his Licence, or by any Member of the Fishery Board who produces a Certificate of his being a Member, or by any Water Bailiff appointed in pursuance of the said Act who produces the instrument appointing him, or by any Constable duly authorised.

Close Seasons: Brown Trout between 30th September and 1st March; Coarse Fish between 14th March and 16th June.
Size Limit—not less than 8 inches from Snout to Fork of Tail.

Thomas Ward bought the fishing rights with their various land purchases. Over the years many customers have had the good fortune to be taken for a day's fishing. There is also a fishing club for employees

Each kiln had a drop out box to collect dust from the kiln exhaust gas. Dust arrestment was not very efficient and many will remember the 'swathe of grey' downwind of the plant. Even in the 1960s, Nick Dinsdale, then an apprentice and later purchasing manager, remembers the trees along West Bradford Road being covered in dust.

The early kilns were of riveted construction. Wilf Hewitt remembers a kiln repair where a new section was inserted using Ribble's own labour. 1,000 rivets per shift was considered a good performance.

Billy (H W) Gilbert, who came from Ketton and supervised construction joinery, had a red setter that occasionally came to work with him. One day Billy took a short cut on his way home and his dog, racing to catch up, jumped over a wall into a slurry basin. Luckily the basin was full and a nearby operator was able to grab the dog by the collar and haul it out; otherwise it would surely have drowned. The dog, now very wet and grey, ran all the way home and made a great mess shaking off the slurry in Billy's house. Billy's son Gerald supervised contractors in the 1980s.

The chimney for kiln 2 was half complete at the time of the 1937 Coronation of George VI and on that day a flag was flown from the top. The workforce was given a day's holiday to celebrate.

William (Bill) Fehrenbach was chief electrician, ex Parry and Elmquist, and lived at Bona Vista almost opposite the works entrance. Early in the war Bill's son Peter remembers huge numbers of trucks being loaded with packed cement for construction of the American airbase at Burtonwood. The drivers were African American GIs who would park their loaded trucks outside the house on West Bradford Road and set off in convoys of up to twenty. An added attraction to Peter was that the drivers

Bill Fehrenbach, chief electrician, with his wife Edna and son Peter in the garden of Bona Vista

Main office on West Bradford Road. The wings were raised to two storeys later.
The single storey building to the right was the construction office, housing S H Bowyer and others

gave him chewing gum. Cement was also supplied to Warton aerodrome, near Blackpool. It was transported at night, mainly by women driving trucks with minimal lights in order to avoid detection.

Derrick Green, son of Fred who was a joiner during the war, remembers taking his father's Sunday lunch to him at work. Then aged 11, he suspended a bowl from each handlebar and cycled in from Salthill Road. In winter the joiners would eat around a red hot stove; for them there was clearly no shortage of firewood.

One of the joiners made a sledge for his children and decided that if he hung it round his neck and wore a large coat he could remove it from the works without being noticed. Turning confidently into Pimlico Road he spotted

Billson waiting at the bus stop, so he quickly crossed the road and kept his head down as he walked by. Next day at work Billson remarked, 'I hope you are well. You seem to have lost a bit of weight since yesterday'.

Bob Hargreaves, who was a shift electrician before the war, left in 1945 because he didn't like shift work. While he was away at war the Company, true to its usual practice at the time, topped up his military wage and paid his mother £1 per week.

In October 1940 Terry Punchard was sampling slurry from a high vantage point on top of one of the silos when he heard an aeroplane. He looked up to see the markings. It wasn't one of ours. Fortunately for Terry the plane continued to the north west and dropped its

Front of Office 1937, left to right Messrs. Hill, Wordsworth, Johnson, R F Stagg, F R Stagg, Bowyer, Parkinson and Bleazard

Hudswell Clarke saddle tank locomotive number 1660, delivered in December 1935

two bombs on Chatburn. Ron Freethy, who advised the works on the nature reserve created for Chatburn school, has discovered that the plane completed three circuits before dropping the bombs. The most likely explanation is that the intended target was Waterloo mill, the home of the gas turbine development work; from the air there must have been a bewildering number of mills and the cement works was clearly not a mill. Some wartime precautions were taken. The floor under what is now the main office reception was strengthened and the basement underneath became an air raid shelter. A small

Kiln 1 'heat exchange' chains, hung in festoons near the upper end of the kiln. Kiln internal diameter is about 2 metres

tunnel was driven from the cellar as an escape route if the building came down. It is still there today, its end marked by a manhole cover.

In that early part of the war there was a real fear of invasion and a plan was made to immobilise the works. The plan involved removing only key bits of equipment sufficient to prevent the plant functioning. In August 1942 Billson was invited to a secret meeting to finalise the plans. To ensure secrecy he had to take his National Registration Identity Card to prove his identity to the police officer at the door.

Mulberry Harbour

Ball mills were used for grinding the raw material into slurry and the clinker and gypsum into cement. Up to 1959 the method of charging the mill was to stop it with the door to one side at about head height and shovel in the charge by hand. As the charge consisted of steel balls between 15 and 90 millimetres in diameter, this was no mean task. It was usually carried out by the packing crew on Sunday overtime.

During the war much research was carried out into reinforced concrete. This culminated in the building of Mulberry harbour sections in a secret operation codenamed Phoenix. Ribble supplied the cement, delivered secretly by night, for the sections made at Lytham Creek. Robin Parkinson's daughter, Betty, on

A mishap with the tippler

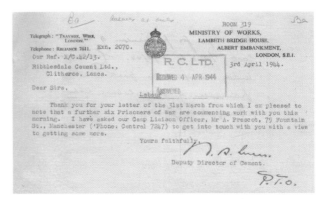

Six POWs to start work at Ribblesdale in April 1944

holiday with the family in Margate remembers seeing sections being towed down the Thames. Her father would not say what they were, only that there was 'our' cement in them.

In 1942 a successful attempt was made to make black cement. The operators added carbon black to the cement mills and became so dirty that their wives began to think that they had married coal miners. The cement was used to make dark coloured runways so as to lessen their visibility and reduce the likelihood of attack. Unfortunately our own pilots couldn't see the runways either, so the experiment was quickly terminated.

In about 1945, Anker Lund, a Dane from F L Smidth who had been working at a cement works in Drogheda Ireland, came as chief chemist. He was a forceful character with friends in high places so he got his ideas implemented and production at Ribblesdale improved significantly. A few years later he returned to Ireland.

During and after the Second World War, when there was a severe shortage of labour, Italian and German prisoners of war were employed.

Town Council visit to the cement works. Loading up for a quarry tour in a modified Horrocksford rail wagon

German prisoners of war cannot have felt too badly about their treatment on the works. They wore no special identification and were not guarded. For Christmas 1946 they created an attractive greeting card, which was posted on the notice board.

Donald Brewer, father of Alan who worked for transport for many years, was in charge of a group of about 20 Italian prisoners of war. He said that there wasn't much work in them but they made excellent coffee!

Otto Volkmer was born in 1926 in Ludwigshaven, about 15 miles from Heidelberg. He was apprenticed as an electrician and attended Technical School. Ludwigshaven was a manufacturing town and Otto's home was destroyed three times by Allied bombing during his apprenticeship.

He joined the army signals, aged 18, and was wounded in August 1944. He remembers that it took six days to

Happy Christmas 1946

travel the short journey from Koblenz to his home in Ludwigshaven. The railway stations in most of the towns were destroyed, so the trains ran only from the outskirts of one town to the outskirts of the next and then only at night. To cross the towns travellers had to walk. In January 1945 he returned to his unit in northern France, near to the D-day landings. Less than a month later and before he was 19 years old he became an American prisoner of war.

Kiln 1

Raw meal in the form of slurry was stored in slurry basins ready for pumping to the kiln. Unless the slurry is agitated it settles out and cannot be pumped. The agitation is achieved by blowing air down pipes right to the bottom of the basin. The pipes here are rotating in groups and the arm on which they are supported moves slowly round on a railway line at the perimeter so that the whole basin is agitated. In later designs the air pipes were fixed to the arms. This worked just as well and was more reliable. The picture shows one basin in operation and one under construction

Town Council visit in 1937. (2) Councillor F Dugdale, journalist, (3) A R Bleazard, borough surveyor, (5) Tim Goodman, borough surveyor, (6) G E Marlow, director RCL, (7) Alderman W Standring, marine store owner, (9) Alderman H Boothman, owner economic stores, (10) F R Stagg, joint MD RCL, (11) Alderman J Thornber, cotton manufacturer, (12) Councillor G Hargreaves, mayor, (14) Joseph Ward, chairman RCL, (15) Alderman J H Satterthwaite, furniture store owner, (18) E Elmquist, consulting engineers Parry and Elmquist, (19) W Harris, borough gas engineer, (20) J H Billson, works manager, (21) A H Todd, borough electrical engineer, (22) Alderman R Manley, auctioneer, (24) H Cahill, accountant RCL, (27) H Wrigley, deputy borough treasurer, (30) J H Taylor, borough treasurer, (32) Councillor F Bentham, cycle shop owner, (34) Bill Lucas, Tunnel, (39) R F Stagg, director RCL, (40) Councillor H Cook, stockbroker, (41) R Y Parkinson, sales manager RCL, (44) S H Bowyer, site engineer Parry and Elmquist

He was taken by Liberty ship to Camp Butler, North Carolina, where he spent a year using his electrical skills. In 1946 he was advised that he was being returned to Germany and was sent by sea via Liverpool. However on arrival he was handed over to the British who were short of skilled labour, so he was detained here. For about twelve months he worked at Andover, loading bombs for the conflict in Malaysia. Then he came to the north as a farm worker, based at a prisoner-of-war camp near Ripon. By then he had no desire to return to Germany, so he joined the Royal Engineers, working on bomb clearance. He was based in Hyde Park during the 1948 Olympics and he learnt to drive heavy equipment such as an RB19 loading shovel at that time.

Train bringing stone from quarry to tippler

PIMLICO, MOORLAND & WEST BRADFORD ROAD DISTRICTS

V.J. PARTY IN THE CANTEEN AT HORROCKSFORD. 25th September, 1945.

He ended up working in a garage near Gisburn, where he met his wife and in 1954 accepted a job as shift electrician at the cement works. He and his wife lived in 1 Chatburn Old Road, later demolished for construction of the link road. His starting wage for seven shifts per week was £13 17s 6d. It was easy to get to work living so close; sometimes he thought too close. Then, as now, working for the cement industry demanded serious commitment.

At the time Otto joined Ribble Cement, kiln 4 was being built and electrostatic filters were being installed on kilns 1 and 2 as part of the planning conditions. He was much in demand to interpret drawings that came in Danish and with measurements in millimetres.

Cement mill 1 and raw mill 1

John Billson was a strong manager who never admitted to dust problems. However on one occasion Otto remembers operators being sent to clean the dust off the benches in Brungerley Park.

Marcin Bialecki, shift foreman, was captured in Poland for breaking a curfew. He was sent to a camp in Austria, where he was trained as a stonemason, and then to a camp in Germany where he was involved in repairing railway lines. After the war he was entitled to a pension from the German government. Otto helped him with the forms and in due course Marcin got his pension. As a result several others also came for help. With the extra money from his pension Marcin regularly travelled to Poland to visit his relatives.

In due course Otto became electrical foreman and then deputy works manager under Paul Livesey. When Paul moved on in 1980 John Adderley invited Otto to apply for the works manager's job. He told the interviewer that the works manager's job was 'to maximise production in a safe and efficient manner'. He got the job! It must say something about the senior management of the cement works that they promoted a former prisoner-of-war to works manager.

Paper was in short supply during the war years so customers who received cement in paper sacks paid extra for the sack; the extra was refunded when the sack was returned for recycling. Jute sacks were reused on a similar basis and in the packing plant women were

Todmorden 27th June 1945. Was Winston Churchill the Ribble cement sales representative in Yorkshire? We have no record that he was, but he would certainly have got the job

Early six-spout rotary packer. As the carousel rotates one hundredweight (50kg) capacity paper sacks are placed manually onto each available spout. As soon as a sack is in place cement is automatically blown into the sack through the spout. Each sack is individually weighed automatically on a balance; the weights can be seen hanging on arms above the carousel. By the time the carousel has rotated about ¾ of a turn the sack is filled to the correct weight and is pushed off automatically onto a conveyor. Modern versions of this packer fill 4,000 25kg sacks per hour, a filling rate of 100 tons per hour

employed, using industrial sewing machines, to repair the jute sacks.

In 1946 seventy Poles were billeted in Low Moor mill, which had been purchased in about 1936 by Ribble Cement. Low Moor was occupied by Royal Engineers during the war and later housed prisoners of war in a hostel. Soon after the prisoners were moved out the Poles, mostly ex Allied Army, were moved in. By 1948, 153 persons and 23 staff were accommodated in the Low Moor hostel. The cement works employed a caretaker there who also, to make best use of his time,

took in food waste from the works canteen and cooked it up as pigswill. Billson kept a few pigs at Rockmount, so his pigs were probably well fed!

Immediately after the war the shortage of labour was acute and the Ministry of Works had responsibility to help provide labour for the cement works in order to help rebuild the country. There is a huge volume of correspondence between the works and the Ministry, all about getting more people. In June 1948 Poles made up 42% of the workforce. Not all stayed because the work was hard and dirty and other jobs were available in the area. Between January and August 1948 sixty-five Poles started and forty-four left, enticed away to jobs in the cotton industry.

One who stayed was Ewald Nerenberg, who resided in the hostel at Low Moor for almost ten years. The 1947 winter was so cold that the Ribble froze over for weeks and the workers from the hostel walked to work on the ice. One tried a bicycle but it proved too difficult to stay upright. Ice skates proved to be the most effective aid to an easy journey to work. Ewald married a local girl and his two sons, Peter and Eric, work in the quarry today.

Peter's son Robert started as an apprentice electrician in 2007, so he represents the third generation of the family. Ewald always believed that he had lost all his family during the war. Very sadly only after his death did the family discover that Ewald's brother and sister were still living in eastern Europe.

Although it became a subsidiary of Ribblesdale, Horrocksford always ran as a separate company and for fifteen years the two had to share Lanehead quarry. At the beginning the quarry was horseshoe shaped, the open end to the south west. It happened that the land

Cabin of 100RB excavator that was damaged in a rock fall and was being returned by Pickfords after repair at Ruston Bucyrus works in early April 1946. It was parked in Woone Lane, Clitheroe, overnight and set off early next morning for Chatburn. Here it is on Chatburn Old Road, having difficulty with a tree. Sam Gate, centre

Peter Nerenberg driving a 16½ ton Fowler bulldozer, purchased new in 1960. The bulldozer was rescued by Bruce Mitchell and Mark Robinson

Tippler in use. Steam crane on rail track

ownership boundary ran through the quarry, roughly in a northerly direction, so each company actually owned part of the quarry. Ribble's extraction rate exceeded Horrocksford's and it was agreed that whenever Ribble overstepped the boundary a royalty would be paid for the stone extracted from Horrocksford's area.

In 1948 record production of just over 3 tons per man hour was achieved in both Lanehead and Bold Venture quarries, a total of 3,700 tons quarried in one week. The quarrymen were paid by the hour and earned up to £12 per week. Blasting created a large triangular pile, with blocks up to a metre cube, against the face. At Horrocksford, quarrymen would pick up the pieces from the base of the pile and load them into Jubilee wagons, small narrow-gauge side-tipping railway trucks. Pieces of stone too large to be broken by sledge hammer were drilled and 'popped' with black powder. This was a highly hazardous practice, now forbidden, as Jimmy Holden found out to his cost when he lost the sight in one eye, damaged by flying debris. Jimmy was the first of three generations of Holdens to work on the site; his grandson John works for maintenance. As the pile was removed at the toe the higher material would avalanche bringing down new material for loading.

Ribble had a Ruston Bucyrus 100RB excavator filling twenty-ton mineral trucks that were then shunted down to the works. For every new blast the standard gauge rail tracks had to be lifted, removed and replaced afterwards. Three Hudswell Clarke steam locomotives were used, each normally pulling eight wagons. Meanwhile at Horrocksford the Jubilee wagons were pushed to the foot of a long slope and joined up into short trains. The trains were then pulled by a long rope winch up to the crusher house to be emptied and returned. In the crusher house were crushers, screens, chutes and line shafting in an arrangement Heath Robinson would have felt at home with. The line shafting was driven by a National gas engine kept immaculate by Sam Robinson, whose son Joe was a well known singer in the local operas and managed the Moorcock Inn, used later by the Company for social occasions.

Bold Venture quarry just west of Chatburn had been purchased by Ribble in 1945. Modern plant was installed at the same time as kiln 3 was being built and in 1951 Horrocksford left their old site near to Isis cement and moved to Bold Venture. Since 1951 almost everyone has referred to the Horrocksford plant in Bold Venture quarry as 'Horrocksford'. Concrete aggregates and black top were manufactured there until the 1990s when the operation closed to conserve limestone resources for cement manufacture. Black top from Horrocksford was used on the Preston bypass, the first section of motorway in the UK.

In 1949 Michael Foot MP, writing in the Daily Herald, called for nationalisation of the cement industry. If that had taken place then this story would certainly be very different.

Ruston Bucyrus RB100 excavator in Coplow quarry in July 1950

Chapter 6
Ribblesdale Cement Works – 1950-1982

The planning permission for kiln 3 stipulated a 340ft (104m) high chimney with the condition that when kilns 1 and 2 had been connected to it, the two old 201ft stacks should be demolished to ground level. However approximately 75ft of each was retained and floors put in 16ft from the top to make extra water tanks. The 340ft chimney cost £30,000 and had a large square platform near the base for the four kiln exhaust fans. It was roofed by the customary asbestos cement sheets. Unfortunately dust collected on the top of the chimney and hardened into large lumps that fell off, perforating the asbestos roof sheets below. Fairly soon the roof was re-covered with strong corrugated steel sheets, taken from wartime Anderson shelters, pressed flat but still showing camouflage paint for some years after.

Celebrating kiln 3 light up July 1951. Left to right, T Allan, wash miller, S Wallace, crane driver and Frank Salwiczek (who did not return to Poland after the war due to the dangerous situation there)

Kiln 3 was commissioned in July 1951. It suffered from rings of clinker building up inside the kiln. Attempts to remove these with long metal poles were not very successful and usually the kiln had to be cooled down to remove them. Leonard Kent, who came to Ribble from Horrocksford in 1942 to work in maintenance, was ex Home Guard and managed to get hold of a Maxim machine gun to shoot out the rings without stopping the kiln. This helped, but eventually some shots went right through the kiln and out the other end. Subsequently an industrial gun was purchased and support brackets were provided on the burner platform of each kiln. Kiln 3, like the other two kilns, also suffered from slurry rings. To remove them without stopping the kiln someone had the bright idea to break them up using explosives. Fred Braithwaite, then quarry manager, discussed this with the explosives supplier and they decided that explosives could be introduced via the sample ports in the kiln. With more than a little trepidation Fred set off the first

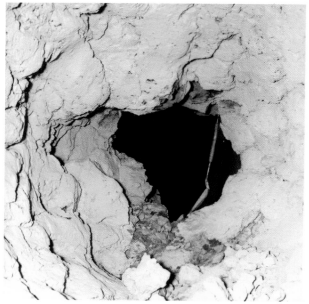

Trouble with kiln build ups. Kiln is three quarters blocked

The Ribble at Brungerley Bridge in 1963; that year the ice was so thick that William Hogg rode his trials bike on it. When the ice began to break up it formed a temporary dam upstream of West Bradford Bridge and the bridge was closed as a precaution. When the ice dam broke the surge was so strong that the ice piled up against the bridge and great rafts of it ended up on the road. The woman and child left centre on the Ribble are Fred Green's daughter-in-law and his grandson John. Fred was a joiner

Light up of kiln 3, 17 July 1951. (2) T Monk, shift foreman, (3) J Cook, fitter, (4) A Hart, kilnhouse foreman, (5) G Hetherington, town clerk, (6) Councillor H Cook, stockbroker, (7) G E Marlow, director of RCL, (8) H Beresford, company secretary and director, (9) J H Billson, works manager, (10) E Scherman, P & E electrical engineer, (11) Brask, FLS erector, (12) ? Frandtsen, FLS, (13) L G Kent, maintenance engineer, (14) Councillor Rushton, printer and Mayor, (15) John Holden, labourer on chimney construction, (16) F Mawman, fitter, (17) A Chappell, welder, (18) S Wallace, crane driver, (19) E Wallhead, deputy chief electrician, (20) J B Parker, assistant chemist, (21) A H Matthews, chief chemist, (22) ? Webb, sales, (23) Hubert E Brown, head storekeeper, (24) H Cahill, chief accountant, (25) F Braithwaite, draughtsman, (26) Arthur ?, (27) Councillor F Dugdale, journalist, (28) W Fehrenbach, chief electrician, (29) J A Eadon, P & E director, (30) Charlie Lloyd, building gang, (31) H Wigglesworth, deputy accountant, (32) F Smithson, Bold Venture salesman, (33) W (Bill) Sharples, packing plant foreman, (34) A Jones, transport department clerk, (35) J Hargreaves, cashier

charge. It seemed to work; however, not long afterwards it was apparent that the kiln shell had distorted so the practice was stopped. Afterwards cylinders charged with high-pressure carbon dioxide were used, now known as Cardox. These were quite successful and much safer. Over several years the problems of ring formation caused by build-up in the kilns reduced, possibly because of improved chemical control or perhaps because the stone quality had changed.

Frances Tomlinson started work in the 1950s and soon after became secretary to Billson, who was the boss from the beginning of operations in 1935/36 up to his retirement in 1962. Under Billson's leadership Ribble was described as the 'star in Tunnel's crown'. Billson was a strong character but by all accounts a very fair man. He set high standards for himself too. One day,

Kiln 3 first light up. Waste wood was used to create sufficient temperature for the powdered coal from the burner to ignite. Today a pilot burner using gas or oil is used. This kiln has a dam ring, a ring of bricks standing proud of the rest near to the kiln outlet, that can just be seen in front of the fire. Dam rings are no longer used in cement kilns. The exit ports, where clinker passes from the kiln into the planetary coolers, can just be seen at the front of the picture

View of the cement works sometime between 1951 and 1965. Note the rafts of stone wagons on sidings that stretch right up to the back of the office block. Behind the cement silos, left centre, can be seen the top of the tippler. In front of the chimney are three slurry basins, to the left of which is a group of six slurry bottles, which were used for pre-blending the slurry. The Horrocksford works, top right, had not yet been demolished

when Frances had typed a letter for him, Billson signed it and called her in. 'I am not happy with my signature', he said, 'please type this again'. Frances' grandfather was George Hargreaves who was Mayor of Clitheroe at the time of the official opening of the works in 1937. On Sundays Billson would walk along Chatburn Old Road, from which vantage point he could see whether the quarrymen were working hard enough.

In 1951 there was again a critical shortage of labour. The Clitheroe Advertiser reported that there were 300 vacancies in the area and only 20 unemployed.

In that year Emilio Conti was living in a farming community not very far from Rome. Farming was not

very prosperous and he was looking for employment further afield. Interviews were being held in Naples by representatives from several countries. He was waiting in the Belgium queue when Wally Russell, who was Ribble's personnel manager, beckoned to him and following an interview and five medicals he came to Ribblesdale. He had little English although he had tried to learn some from a friend in Italy who had been a prisoner of war at Skipton. Thirty Italians were brought over together by Eastwoods Ltd and were housed in Moreton Hall, between Whalley and Great Harwood, a building that in wartime had been used for training members of the Polish army. Eastwoods advised that the men would arrive hungry and poorly clad and that provision for their welfare would be very necessary. However, Moreton Hall was far from luxurious and the food was poor, especially the quantity, as rationing was still in force at that time. At a dance in Whalley a local girl told Emilio about the fish and chip shop and his hunger problems were thereby resolved. He quickly showed all the others how to buy fish and chips and everyone felt a good deal better. Later he moved to more convenient accommodation at Low Moor hostel.

Emilio worked shifts in the crushing plant, which at that time consisted of the tippler, jaw crusher and various conveyor belts. Coal and gypsum were also put through the system and cleaning before each product change was very important. Billson was a stickler for checking that everything was done right and would have the work inspected. One day Billson gave him a brown envelope with a ten shilling note inside 'for doing a good job'. On another occasion Billson had Italian visitors to the factory and invited Emilio to join them for dinner at Stirk House after the visit.

Emilio's wife Rose was a forewoman weaver, also working shifts, at Shawbridge mill. It was difficult to manage with two young children so Emilio asked his foreman for a day job in the packing plant. The response was negative, so Rose wrote to Billson explaining their difficulties. Two days later Emilio was told that he was being transferred to the packing plant, where he remained for the rest of his career. Prior to mechanisation it was not easy work. Two men would stand on the back of a lorry and a chute

Ruston Bucyrus RT27 well-hole drill, also known as a churn drill, powered by electricity. The drill is on the cable hanging down the hole. On a separate rope is the baler, which at intervals was used to bale out the slurry from the bottom of the hole. When new drilling machines were purchased, two of these churn drills were sent to Bihar, India to drill for water

Jane Ghosh, laboratory manager, with a Ribble customer sample sack and the modern Castle equivalent

The logo from the balcony at the front of the office, saved from a skip by John Haworth when the balcony rails were demolished

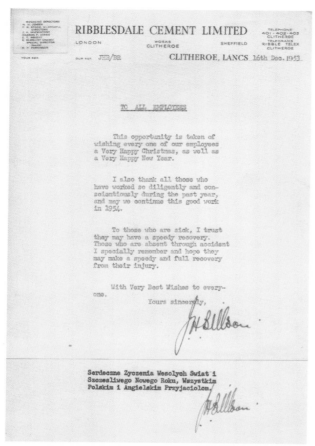

Billson Christmas greetings 1953 in English and Polish

not very well supported. The Divisional Education Officer of Lancashire Education Committee wrote to the Company threatening to discontinue the class unless attendance improved.

Francis (Mike) Kelly, living in Pennsylvania, is one of many who responded to a request in Open Door, the Company newsletter, for historical information. He worked in the laboratory in the 1950s and played for the works football team. He knew Poles, Ukrainians, White Russians, and Yugoslavs all working at the plant in a variety of jobs. It took no time at all before they were proficient and had learned enough English to get by. The Ribble cement works was a veritable United Nations during this period. Peter Geldard, who worked in production for most of his career ending up as production manager, recalls a White Russian, known as Rusky, living in the old Coplow lime works weighbridge house near Rockmount. One day Rusky broke his leg and when, after treatment, he was helped back to his humble home, he found that it had been broken into. Very crestfallen he shuffled across the room and kicked an upturned bucket that he used as a seat. His whole face broke into a broad smile when he discovered that his life savings, hidden under the bucket, had not been touched.

In December 1953 Billson put up a notice wishing everyone a happy Christmas. There were three versions, English, Polish and Italian.

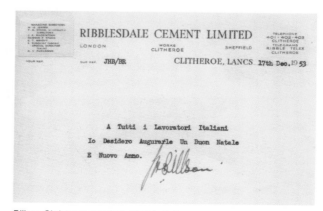

Billson Christmas greetings 1953 in Italian

brought down each hundredweight sack to chest height. The skill was to catch the bag with minimal lifting and steer it into a neat stack on the truck. Sometimes, as a bit of a joke, someone would lubricate the chute and the sack would slide down so fast that it nearly knocked you over. Each truck was loaded with 10 tons, 200 sacks each twice as heavy as today's 25kg ones. The packing team rotated the work so they stacked two trucks and then rested for the next.

More Italian workers came in 1960 and these were accommodated in Low Moor. E Terracini, the Consul for Italy based in Liverpool, arranged for his welfare officer to speak to this group, offering help and support. The Company arranged English classes but they were

Coplow quarry was leased from Clitheroe Corporation and worked by Horrocksford to produce 'white' limestone that was popular for domestic 'gravel' drives. It was also used as aggregate in concrete on Blackpool promenade. The lease ran out in the early 1940s and Ribble agreed to purchase Coplow in exchange for Cross Hill quarry, which was essentially worked out, and £400. The Company wanted Coplow as a water reservoir that could be used if the River Ribble was too low in the summer. The quarry was deepened by 20ft using a Ruston Bucyrus 54RB excavator that had been delivered early for Horrocksford

Bold Venture. Later a much larger 100RB was used. The stone from Coplow was used as a raw material in the cement works. A pipeline was installed from the river, but the first 18ft of the excavation filled up from natural springs so the pipeline was hardly used. The capacity was in excess of 12 million gallons. Youngsters began to use the quarry for swimming, so for safety reasons it was eventually fenced off and a padlocked gate fitted.

In 1953 floods devastated the east coast of England. Ribblesdale contributed £2,500 of the £10,000 raised

Front-of-office, probably late 1950s (1) Fred Braithwaite, (2) Jim Kernick, (3) Ted Brown, (4) Bert Pemberton, (5) John A Edon, (6) Arthur Matthews, (7) Harry Milne, (8) Bill Demain, (9) George Speak, (11) Jim Ainsworth, (12) Richard Roberts, (13) Walter Blunt, (14) Billy Gilbert, (15) Les Dixon, (16) George Thompson, (18) John Birchenough, (19) Michael Poland, (20) Len Garner, (21) Bill Dixon, (22) Arthur Jones, (23) Harold Wigglesworth, (24) John Adderley, (25) Fred Smithson, (26) Aubrey Lord, (27) Jack Hargreaves, (28) Mary Leigh (Miller), (29) Carole McCally (Wright), (30) Ann Hodkinson, (31) Eileen Walne, (32) Elsie Simpson (Lord), (33) Jean Pickup, (35) Betty Rawsthorne (Dewhurst), (36) Frances Hanson (Tomlinson), (37) J H Billson, (38) Mrs Billson, (39) Rawson F Stagg, (40) Judith Woodhead (Birchenough), (41) Anne Perrings (Hall), (42) Edith Limbert, (43) Margaret Knowles (Stott), (44) Barbara Chatburn (Harrison)

22 ton capacity dump truck supplied by Douglas, a Thomas Ward company. William Hogg was one of the drivers. Prior to the completion of the crushing plant in the mid 1960s the stone was tipped into rail wagons in the area near the western end of the raw materials gantry and the rail wagons were then discharged using the tippler

locally towards the national appeal. The Company's generosity was prompted by the clearing of the debt on the third kiln.

From 1949 to 1955 the works supplied 140,000 tons of cement to the Manchester Corporation Haweswater Aqueduct Scheme. Two tunnels in Bowland were the principal destination of this cement.

The Works was effectively run by the three local managers, John Billson, Robin Parkinson (local area director) and Horace Cahill, the accountant. Sadly Cahill became seriously ill and in 1959 Brian White came to the works to replace him. Brian was one of several talented sportsmen who have worked at Ribble. He previously played hockey for Northumberland and Durham and later became president of Lancashire County Hockey Association in its 100th year. He and his wife Evelyn moved over from Leeds into a small cottage on farmland that Ribble had just purchased. Mr and Mrs Billson had gone to the cottage to receive the removal men while Brian drove Evelyn and their young children. By the time the family arrived the Billsons had all the furniture put into the right places and had lit a log fire; what a wonderful welcome.

CALAMITY CHARLIE

Calamity Charlie's been at it again
His coat flying loose got caught on
a chain,
He pulled himself free and fell over
a stack
Of scaffolding planks he'd forgot to
put back.
He picked himself up and went down
once more
In a pool of thick oil he had left
on the floor.
In fact, it's a wonder the fellow's alive;
Calamity Charlie's in Ward No.5!

Use the other side for Ken Kareful

KEN KAREFUL

Ken Kareful clocks in, a few minutes to spare,
He goes to his bench, all is tidy on there;
He selects the right tools and makes sure
they're O.K;
He gets on with the job, and then clears away
When he's finished. Leaves nothing to cause
folk to trip,
No holes to fall into, no ladders to slip.
Ken Kareful, thats him, he's a right "gradely" lad,
If we follow his steps we shan't do so bad.

Use the other side for Calamity Charlie
Make sure you have signed your form, then hand it in to your works
within the next fortnight.

Printed by Cement and Concrete Association, London S W 1

1957 safety competition entry from James York

Selling cement was often done in a social setting, such as at dinner with the customer. Robin Parkinson's wife Lyn, who was well liked, excelled in that environment and may have been responsible for even more cement sales than her husband.

In the mid 1960s millions of people in Bihar, India, were in danger of dying because of a severe water shortage. The Rotary Clubs took this up under the banner of Water Aid. Rotarian Eric Walmsley recalled that in the Clitheroe area pumping equipment was promised but no-one could afford the cost of drilling rigs. John Adderley, ex Parry and Elmquist, was now manager of the works. When he found out, he donated two drilling rigs that had just been replaced with new ones, so the scheme went ahead and many lives were saved. Several suppliers had bid to supply the new drilling rigs for the works. Reich Drills put on a very professional demonstration and promised a drilling rate of three holes per day. With great embarrassment to Reich, all they achieved with Ribble's hard stone was 6 feet per day. Halco drills from Halifax were purchased instead.

It was soon evident that still more cement was required and an application was put in for fourth kiln, which eventually started production in May 1961.

In 1960/61 Bellman quarry and farm, tenanted by Rennie Hargreaves, was purchased at auction for future stone and clay reserves at a cost of £25,000. Six years later the Collinson family took over as tenants. From 1827 to 1870 the farm house, situated on the turnpike, had been the Bellman Inn, also known as the Old Bellman. On the opposite side of the road, in the direction of Park House, was a racecourse, no sign of which remains. There are records of Clitheroe Borough Races taking place in 1835 and 1837 over the new turf at Hardhill Park, Hardhill being the old name for Bellman. The races were described as sweepstakes and the 1837 programme states that 'No gambling will be allowed and all vagrants and disorderly people will be arrested'. An earlier 'Clithero Races' was held on Horrocksford pastures in 1823.

In 1960 the Company was again desperately short of workers and sent someone to Liverpool to interview potential recruits. Out of 98 interviewed 32 were deemed suitable for work. Most worked less than a month, saying that they were unhappy with the hostel. One left because he was paying too much income tax and just three stayed for a month, the final stalwart leaving six months later.

Mohammed Amin came to England from Pakistan in 1962 aged twenty; he came in response to British Government requests for people from the Commonwealth to help overcome a serious shortage of labour. He spoke no English, but after six months attending night school and with help from his work colleagues he was fluent. He came to the cement works a couple of years later and then took six months unpaid leave to return to Pakistan to be married. In 1967 he started full time at the cement works.

In 1968 there was no paternity leave, so when his wife was close to giving birth Amin called home from the works pay phone every hour to check on her condition.

After the fifth call he was advised that his wife had gone into labour. He quickly arranged time off and walked the three miles home but, by the time he arrived, his wife had been taken to Whalley. She couldn't wait though, and delivered a healthy baby boy in the ambulance just as she arrived at the hospital.

Amin came from a farming community not far from Gujarkhan, which is about 40km north of Islamabad. His family lived six miles from the nearest town and there was no transport. He had to walk three miles each way to school every day. Mohammed Ashrif, Mohammed Riaz and Daulatzar Khan came to the cement works from the same area. At one time Riaz was even on the same shift as Amin. In 1986 Amin had a bad accident at work and during his rehabilitation he attended Blackburn College where he obtained O level and A level Urdu and a teaching diploma for community teaching. For 14 years he did two jobs. As well as the cement job, he taught 'Urdu' and 'English for non-English speakers' at Blackburn College. His Urdu students included people from the social services. He also worked as a volunteer for the Citizens Advice Bureau for four years and still does similar informal work as he is known locally within the small Asian community in Clitheroe. Amin and his wife have six children, all of whom attended Clitheroe Royal Grammar school and all of whom are university graduates.

22 ton capacity dump truck supplied by Douglas, a Thomas Ward company. Frank Metcalfe was one of the drivers. The NCK excavator was driven by Peter Lapik

Euclid dump truck being loaded by a Ruston Bucyrus 110RB driven by Eric Nerenberg

Amin and his Asian colleagues were much in demand at Christmas because, unlike many, they were happy to work Christmas Day. One Christmas in the late 1970s Amin operated kilns 1 to 5 on his own for twelve hours, an astonishing achievement. Later the works manager gave him £3 in a brown envelope for his trouble. He wasn't quite sure how to respond. Even then £3 was not a princely sum.

Amin was an early member of the Trades Union and at one meeting, to his utter astonishment, Fred Braithwaite greeted him in Urdu.

In the 1960s welfare facilities on the works were rather limited. The works meeting minutes during this time routinely recorded that there were no problems or complaints from the quarry. The secretary diligently recording this fact was blissfully unaware that there were no facilities whatsoever in the quarry. There were no washing facilities near the kilns either and drinking water had to be collected in bottles from some distance. Washing was done in the cooling water from the kiln bearings, fine in winter when hot water was welcome but not so good in a hot summer. People hung their towels on the hand rails, where they dried in the radiated heat from the kiln shell.

Red hot lumps of clinker from kilns 1 and 2 had to be broken up with a 14 pound hammer. It was a very strenuous task, so Otto Volkmer suggested using a jack hammer; this was tried, but the point of the hammer went soft at high temperature and became useless. Fred Braithwaite decided that a crusher would be better and wrote to Wards. They asked for a sample and Fred sent a large piece. The technical people at Wards tested the strength of the lump by dropping it on the floor, where it broke into a thousand pieces. When Fred received this news from Wards he replied immediately, 'forget the crusher, send asbestos gloves'. Later a second hand Broadbent crusher from Horrocksford was installed. When Fred was in charge of maintenance he used to visit all areas of the works with the local maintenance fitters and make notes in his book. The fitters called it Fred's 'forgetting book'. Such is the lot of a maintenance manager, there is always much more work to do than time and money will permit.

Peter Geldard started in the time office. One of his tasks was to distribute the hand washing gel, Swarfega, from the top store. Each production worker was allowed eight ounces per week but maintenance people received ten ounces. It was all carefully weighed, but you could buy extra if you wanted. He also issued one new donkey jacket, with RCL painted on back, per person per year

in exchange for a worn out one. Such is the enterprise of ordinary people that, despite this, you could still buy a new RCL donkey jacket on Clitheroe market. Peter then moved onto the works and in due course became kiln house foreman and finally production manager. He remembers that during a kiln repair a fitter stuck his head out of a kiln door and gave his foreman a mouthful of abuse. Fred Braithwaite was walking by and overheard. He sent the fitter home!

In 1962 George Stanley, a knowledgeable amateur geologist and palaeontologist, previously recruited to Ribblesdale staff by Billson, joined forces with Fred to produce a report assessing the Company's stone reserves.

Part of the collection of Stanley Westhead, a nationally known specialist on the crinoid and blastoid fossils of the Waulsortian mud mounds of the Clitheroe area, is exhibited at Clitheroe museum. One crinoid genus found at Coplow is named *Pimlicocrinus*, after nearby Pimlico.

More production was required and an application was made for a fifth kiln with all associated machinery and a second chimney. This application went to a Public Enquiry. The Alkali inspector asked for the stack to be 400ft tall, which the Planning Authority thought unacceptable alongside the existing 340ft chimney. As a compromise a stainless steel venturi was fitted inside the top of the chimney in the belief that this would direct the plume higher. It did not achieve the desired effect and was later removed. The then Lord Clitheroe told the Public Enquiry that some years previously he had refused an offer of £100,000 for Worsaw Hill. The offer had been made by a company in the extractive industry, but not by Ribble Cement. Times have changed; a proposal to quarry Worsaw Hill would now be unthinkable.

In anticipation of kiln 5 and a substantial increase in production, the quarry was transformed. The rail tracks were removed and large dump trucks obtained to tip directly into the new crushing plant. A winter hazard affecting the railway lines was thus eliminated, namely the effect of frost, at the first sign of which men were despatched, with bags of salt, to all the railway points to prevent them freezing.

During the early 1960s the sidings were always filled up with fully loaded rail wagons before the quarry finished for the day. This allowed the jaw crusher and tippler to operate almost 24 hours per day but even then crushing could hardly keep up with the kilns. It was difficult but the works soldiered on until the new crushing plant was built in 1965-66.

Moving the wagons wasn't always very safe. Little Charlie, a Pakistani, was in charge of shunting the rail wagons onto the sidings behind the office. The lines were downhill, so each truck was allowed to run down under gravity, its speed limited by a brake stick. Trying to save time at the end of his shift, Charlie let three wagons go together. The brake stick failed to control the wagons and soon he fell over in his efforts to slow them down. The wagons careered into the stop at the rail end and piled up like a tepee. Fortunately there was no-one nearby, but it was a close shave for the office block.

The new crushing plant had a new Sheepbridge crusher but the old jaw crusher and hammer mills were also relocated within the new plant. Ronnie Evans, later crushing plant foreman, drove the overhead crane to help with the construction, but the steel structure that supported the crane was only half completed and the crane had to be powered from a trailing cable instead of from a proper supply alongside the crane rails. To stop him driving the crane off the end of the incomplete crane rails some old kiln chains were wrapped round the rails as stops.

Management are often quick to claim that a new project is being commissioned, even when the installation of equipment is incomplete. It is probably because project timetables are always ambitious. The new crushing plant was supposed to be finished by the end of 1966, so over Christmas two dumper loads of stone were put through the crusher even though there was no conveyor to take the crushed stone away. The stone ended up in a large pile in the basement and the mess had to be cleared up later, but management could at least claim that commissioning had started before year end.

Mill relocated from Ketton to become raw mill 5 in the early 1990s

Chains being fitted to the upper part of kiln 6. The chains are tied back for access purposes. Normally they hang down two thirds of the diameter of the kiln. In operation the hot gas passing through the kiln heats up the chains hanging in the gas stream; then, as the kiln turns, the hot chains collapse into the slurry and powdered raw material in the bottom of the kiln and give up their heat. In this way the maximum heat is extracted from the gas and the kiln makes the most efficient use of heat energy

Amadeo Loi came from Sardinia in a group of forty via Naples and Milan. After four years at the Shireburn Arms in Hurst Green, he joined the cement works. His English was quite good before he came but it improved when he taught Paul Livesey's aunt Italian and she taught him English in exchange. Amadeo served 37 years; his father-in-law Richard Catlow drove a delivery truck and brother-in-law Martin Catlow worked in the quarry. Amadeo's son Andrew now works on the kilns.

Kiln 5 followed not long after the new crushing plant producing its first clinker in October 1967.

Sheila Haywood ARIBA FILA was a nationally acclaimed landscape architect who was one of the first to work on quarry restoration. In the late 1960s it was she who produced the first plan with Chatburn Old Road quarried away. She said that if the road had remained it

would have been a feature drawing the attention to the quarried area. The quarry now merges into the general landscape, as anyone who climbs Pendle Hill can testify. The approved scheme included restoration of Lanehead as a lake, the estimated volume of which was then 4,000,000,000 gallons. In November 1971 a legal agreement was made between Ribble, Horrocksford and Richard Briggs and Sons Ltd, later to become Tarmac, to implement the scheme. William (Bill) Hogg, son of Ken and father-in-law of process engineer Rob Davy, worked in the quarry for more than 25 years. He drove a variety of mobile equipment and planted vast numbers of trees in accordance with Sheila Haywood's plan. One day he received a phone call from Billson inviting him to the main office. Billson came out, shook his hand, and gave him his 25 year gold watch, as was the custom at the time for factory workers. Today 25 years awards, to all employees, are made at a night out.

Keith Hall trained as a bricklayer stonemason and joined the quarry in 1973. Keith proposed to his future wife Mary in the leafy shade of Chatburn Old Road, a popular spot for courting couples. When Mary told her father, it turned out that he had proposed to her mother in the same place. A few years later, as shot firer, Keith blasted away that very same part of Chatburn Old Road, breaching it for the first time. Keith is a keen campanologist and has rung the old year out and the new one in for the past 39 years. When extras were required for the BBC series 'Born and Bred', filmed near his home in Downham, Keith soon volunteered; he can be seen riding his 1953 BSA bantam motorcycle down the main street. Keith became quarry manager following the retirement of Angus MacKechnie in 1997 and, at the same time, was chairman of the Lancashire branch of the Institute of Quarrying. He became a magistrate in 1986. He also served one term as parish councillor for Chatburn, Downham and Twiston.

Pneumatic bricking rig, used for completing the top half of each ring of refractory bricks. Small air powered pistons hold up every brick until the last brick is put in. Then the arch makes the bricks self supporting. No mortar is used. All the bricks are tapered, just as in a stone archway

Peter Parkes and Malcolm Sowden assessing the remaining thickness of the refractory brick kiln lining. This used to be done by drilling holes through to the metal kiln shell

Some people get nicknames that stick. Brian Allison, construction engineer, when faced with a question would often reply 'I'll get back to you'. Boomerang someone said, and for the rest of his working life Boomerang he was.

John Ridgway, later a shift manager, and Lionel Nash, who worked in the laboratory, were two people who came to Ribble from Limmer and Trinidad in the early 1970s. John telephoned Harry Armstrong, personnel department, who asked him how tall he was. Puzzled, John replied "5 feet 9 inches"; "start on Monday," said Harry, so he did.

Keith Hall in Downham on his BSA bantam.
Keith appeared on his bike in 'Born and Bred'

BoBo diesel bought from Scottish Rail by John Adderley, eventually sold for a nominal sum to the North York Moors railway

Shift men tend to use their initiative, particularly on nights when there are few managers about. The mess rooms were originally very limited and someone invented a recipe for a night time snack. Place a shovel full of hot clinker, straight off kiln 5, in a bucket; add a potato wrapped in foil, top up with clinker and leave for an hour. Baked potato with a tin of beans was a meal fit for a king. After mess rooms had been provided John (known as Will) Koral, chargehand, left his meal in the oven to cook. When he returned an hour or so later his meal had mysteriously transformed into a kiln refractory brick. Someone had a lovely meal at his expense.

In the early 1970s labour turnover was again high. In one record month there were 29 new starters and 31 leavers.

In 1972 the miners' strike led to the three day week and a shortage of coal. In just three weeks the technology for oil burning was copied from Pitstone cement works. Harry Barnett, workshop foreman, had steam boiler experience so he set up heavy oil burning for kilns 3 and 4 and light oil burning for kiln 2. Kilns 3 and 4 ran a couple of months on oil in order to compare costs with

coal burning. At the same time there was a daily limit on electricity usage or a large fine had to be paid. Every evening at 10.00pm Paul Livesey and Otto Volkmer would check the meters in the substation and decide how many mills could be operated until midnight without exceeding the limit.

January 15th 1973 was a great day for the residents of Pimlico. The Clitheroe bypass, completed in 1970, was finally connected to the works via the link road and huge volumes of lorry traffic no longer passed by their front doors. 'The Relief of Pimlico' was the dramatic headline in the Clitheroe Advertiser.

Kiln 6 was commissioned in 1976. This was the last wet process kiln built in the UK. It produced about 1,100 tons per day of clinker and cost about £5.5M, just 10% over budget.

Tunnel and Wards had an uneasy relationship, right from the beginning when they appointed different consultants. It wasn't all out war but it wasn't joint leadership either. In 1981/1982 Wards tried to take over Tunnel, but Derek Birkin, chairman of Tunnel, outwitted Wards by bringing in RTZ as a white knight. As a result both companies were bought by RTZ in 1982. Derek Birkin, later Sir Derek, went on to become chairman of RTZ. It was he who earlier had appointed Alan Tetlow as managing director of Ribble. Tetlow was based at the works, a great improvement on the previous situation where there had been no managing director and the chairman was based elsewhere. Tetlow was a highly professional manager and the driving force behind kiln 7. He insisted on proper estimates for work and it was mainly due to his leadership that kiln 7 was built on time and on budget.

In Tetlow's time efforts were made to export cement. One shipload of cement was despatched from a south coast port to Egypt for a project run by McAlpines. The boat was reported overdue and Jonathan Dale made strenuous efforts to locate the ship. It turned out that the ship had called at Cyprus and received an offer for a more profitable cargo. The cement was tipped into the sea and the ship departed with the new cargo. The ship was eventually located and the master arrested, but it took three years for compensation to be paid. Other exports were more successful logistically but none made a worthwhile profit.

Les Baker drove a quarry dumper. One day, while waiting to be loaded, he saw the quarry face begin to slip and drove quickly out of harm's way. His workmate, Terry Steer, was not so lucky and a large amount of rock fell onto his CAT245 loading shovel, right over the cab. Les feared the worst but as he approached he saw some movement. When Les and Harold Sharples had finally extricated Terry from the cab, it turned out that he had escaped with just a few scratches. The cab was a write off.

Peter Walker, later chief engineer, remembers how the attitude to safety changed at about this time. Peter used to climb a ladder, scramble onto the top of the kiln and walk along the kiln to mark various survey points so that kiln alignment could be checked. Today we use a laser for this task and do not subject people to such risk. Peter retired early in the 1990s and ever since has been leading walking and climbing groups all over the world. One Christmas Eve the group arrived in Sri Lanka and spent the night in a beach hotel. On Christmas Day they set off into the hills. Twenty four hours later, for this was 2004, the tsunami struck and the hotel was utterly destroyed.

Fishing club outing, left to right, front, John Bridges, Keith Malone, middle, Ian Darbyshire, Keith Whittaker, Brian Turner, Terry Steer, Chris Hosker, back, Phillip Helsin, Mark Bennettt

Chapter 7
Ribblesdale Cement Works
– 1983 to present

Kiln 7, installed at a cost of about £30M, was the first precalciner kiln in the UK, so in less than ten years Ribble progressed from old technology to the new without any intermediate stages. There was considerable nervousness about the ability of the new kiln to deal with the high sulfur raw materials from Lanehead quarry. In the event the kiln functioned well and the bypass, installed to deal with the sulfur problem, stood idle. The F L Smidth project manager for the new kiln was Peter Weller. Later he joined Castle Cement and served as managing director from 2003 to 2007.

The commissioning of kiln 7 in 1983 ushered in a new era, more controversial than ever before. If there was

Dave Pomfret's 1994 photograph of John Steed, electrician's mate. This photograph won many competitions representing Ribblesdale camera club and was runner up in a national magazine competition

This 1986 cartoon, of kiln 7 preheater tower, was carried in the torchlight procession celebrating 800 years since the building of Clitheroe castle

one trigger for the excitements and traumas of the next decade, it was the end of the Common Price Agreement on 12 February 1987. Until that time an official cartel had been in operation and the cement price agreed nationally. This created a generally prosperous industry insulated from the influences of economic recessions. When sales volumes reduced the prices stayed the same and the impact on profitability could be accommodated. Prior to 1987, both Ribble and Ketton had used that prosperity to invest in new highly efficient technology. When the next economic downturn occurred in the

Malcolm Copley produced twelve sketches for the 1986 Ribble calendar. Cement mills are loaded to one third full with charge, which consists of steel balls up to the size of a cricket ball. The charge is delivered in 45 gallon drums, each weighing a ton

early 1990s, not only did the sales volume drop but the price dropped dramatically as the cement producers sought to maintain sales volume. The result was a near catastrophic loss of profitability that forced major cost cutting through reduced numbers employed and through use of lower cost fuels.

John Denton, as general manager, and Peter del Strother, as works manager came to Ribblesdale in the late 1980s largely unaware of the changes that would have to be made. Both believed that the works should have a closer relationship with its neighbours so an open day was planned and took place in 1990. About 1,500 people visited the works. Dave Pomfret, shift electrician, produced a stunning slide tape presentation of the wildlife on the quarry. It received high praise from all the visitors. Dave has taken many of the modern photographs in this book. In addition school visits were encouraged with the aim that every child in a local school should have the opportunity to visit the works at least once in his or her education. Castle followed this up later by creating a lively web site specifically designed for schools.

Les Young, an instrument mechanic, owned a corner shop in Rishton. At work, with management's tacit approval, he ran a kiosk on the kiln platform selling cigarettes. There were queues every morning waiting for him to open up. Bob Davy, who was Les' apprentice, said that serving at the kiosk was one of the first jobs he was taught. It was tricky when Les wasn't present because there was always someone who had no money with them and claimed that it would be all right with Les if they paid later. Bob soon learnt that this was no way to run a business. Cash on the nail became the only acceptable means of payment.

At that time there were no computers, so process data was recorded graphically onto paper charts using instruments made by companies such as Chessell and Cambridge Instruments. Paper about 100mm wide was drawn off one reel at very slow speed onto another and pens traced the values of kiln speed, exhaust temperature etc. on the paper as it passed under the pens. You ended up with at least a metre of chart every day and a routine job changing the paper. Bob remembers filling eye drop bottles with ink so that he could perform the delicate task of topping up the ink without making a mess. The main kiln chart recorder, made by Penny and Giles, had thirty pens across its metre and a half width.

Peregrine watch team: (1) Craig Woodcock – Chatburn Police Constable, (2) Brian Hodgson, (3) David Mercella, (4) Brian Turner, (5) John Burgess, (6) Les Baker, (7) Ian Singleton, (8) Jeffrey Robinson, (9) Eric Nerenberg, (10) Keith Hall, (11) Peter Nerenberg, (12) Alan Smith, (13) Terry Steer, (14) Paul Dewhurst, (15) Barry Dean

Children from Chernobyl pictured with, amongst others, Back row:- young lady (group minder), Brian Race (Hyndburn Pallets), M Khan, Heather Hutchins, Ian Johnson, Keith Whittaker, John Ridgway, Peter Nelson, Susan Ormand, Bruce Pollard, all from Ribblesdale. The blonde lady in front of Bruce is Margaret Ferrant (canteen manageress); the lady next to her is Debi Hothersall (purchasing)

In 1986 news of the disaster at Chernobyl became public. In 1996, when twenty children from Chernobyl visited Clitheroe, funds were raised on the works to provide them with clothes, shoes and football hats and scarves. Leading lights in this venture were John Ridgway, Bruce Pollard, Susan Ormand, Bernard Stanley, Ian Johnson and Mukhtar Khan.

Peregrine falcons had tried to raise young in the quarry several times, but it seemed that someone was killing the young birds. Brian Turner, long time senior shop steward who then worked in the quarry, was one of a group who asked if a twenty-four hour watch could be kept. A team of volunteers supervised the nest and a young peregrine successfully hatched and fledged. This watch continued for several seasons and on one occasion a man with a gun was found in the quarry. He claimed that he was

Spotted flycatcher – a common sight on stumps around the quarry

sighting his gun as this was the nearest safe place to his home to do it. The police were advised. One bumper year, those who started early would regularly hear the mewing of three young peregrines hunting pigeons over the works. It may be tough on the pigeons, but they are something of a pest. Peregrines now play a welcome part in the community of wildlife found in the quarry.

In the early 1990s the rail company advised that the cement train to Newcastle was uneconomic and cancelled the service. The Company tried hard to overturn the decision. Johnathan Dale, then northern area director, went to a select committee of Parliament to plead Ribble's case but to no avail. In consequence rail to Clyde was also stopped and delivery of about 250,000 tons of cement per year was transferred to road. The trucks to Glasgow each did two trips per day, 6 days per week, almost 250,000 miles per year! A truck, with a fax and phone on board, would set off northwards from Ribble. If a customer was identified while the truck was en route the truck driver would be directed to deliver straight to the customer. If no customer was identified then the load would be delivered to Clyde depot at Gartsherrie. The large number of direct deliveries saved Castle a lot of money because of reduced double handling.

In 1991 Castle was suffering from reduced sales volumes and severely reduced prices. It was a very difficult time for managers and workforce alike. Pitstone works was closed and Ribble and Padeswood made major cuts in numbers employed. Over just a few years the number employed on the Ribble works was reduced from 400 to 260. Although many volunteered for redundancy there were 35 people who lost their jobs compulsorily through no fault of their own. Those remaining had to adopt new working practices, so there was much change for all. At the same time Ribble became the first cement works in the UK to make serious use of alternative fuels, starting with Cemfuel, a waste solvent based fuel, in 1992; also stone reserves were short and it became necessary to apply to reopen Bellman quarry.

John Livingston was sales and transport manager. One day a customer asked him for a cement sample and rather than delay by returning to the works he went to the local builder's merchant and bought a 50kg bag. He opened the boot of his new company car and as he leant forward to place the bag inside, the upward pointing boot catch neatly cut the bag underneath and the whole contents emptied into the boot. The cement was still warm and fresh, so it spread out like a bag of flour dropped on the kitchen floor. John rushed home, scooped out what he could and finished the job off with

Green Woodpecker in the restored margins of the quarry

Roller mill, kiln 7. This grinds 230 tons per hour of raw material into a fine powder. The two maintenance men are standing on the grinding table. Three 45 ton wheel-like rollers, temporarily removed for maintenance, sit on the table, which rotates when the mill is in operation. The triangular frame, seen above the two men, locks the three wheels in position and three hydraulic rams, operating at 140 atmospheres pressure, pull the frame down, increasing the effective weight of the rollers

One of the rollers in kiln 7 roller mill

the vacuum cleaner. We never found out whether he told his wife, but the vacuum cleaner began to make very sickly noises and within a week he had to buy a new one.

Paul Stevens, for a few years process engineer and now working for the Environment Agency, was a keen rock climber. One lunch break he went free climbing at Cross Hill and fell, knocking himself out and destroying half his

A crane lifts the first section of the stack extension in the early 1990s. The tube is 7.5m long by 3.15m diameter. Another will be lifted on top resulting in a final stack height of 96 metres

1990 Open Day, left to right: Heather Hutchins, David Holgate, Mark Broadley, Len Barber, Carol Grainger (now working for computer services), Eddie Ireland, Roger Cottam, Alan Clarke, Pauline Walker, Peter Geldard, John Ridgway, Stuart Robinson. Alan Clarke received a BEM for his voluntary service as head of Clitheroe Fire Brigade

for several weeks, he did not have any time off work and was only put off climbing for a year or two. Part of the quarry used to be called Dangerous quarry; now he knows why! Heaven knows what today's safety focused management would make of rock climbing.

The introduction of Cemfuel proved to be controversial. The Company consulted its workforce and the Ribble Valley Borough Council before starting, in the belief that such consultation would be sufficient. That belief was mistaken and almost five years of high public profile followed. Peter del Strother attended many public meetings and appeared on local radio, national television, the north west BBC 6 o'clock news live and on Radio 4's Face the Facts with John Waite; he was even mentioned in Hansard. What the Company had failed to do was to make sufficient effort to inform and convince local people. As a result the Company took on a public relations manager at head office in Birmingham

climbing helmet. He struggled back to work and then to the local hospital where he was put on a back board and sent to Blackburn. Although in considerable pain

Demolition of kiln 5

Mark Harwood with one of the latest tankers in the fleet. New tankers are fitted with satellite tracking, a telephone, man down alarm (which sets off the truck flashers and alarm if the driver falls when out of his cab), personal PDA (which holds individual data on delivery point and weight ticket information) and a digital tacho (which is personalised to each driver via a plastic card with microchip)

and the local newsletter 'Open Door' was conceived. About 15,000 copies of each issue are delivered to local addresses, typically twice a year. This approach was followed at the other works and has resulted in much more positive public perceptions.

What the Company had also failed to recognise was the considerable damage that its use of Cemfuel was doing to the merchant incinerator industry. In the early 1990s that industry was indicating that five new incinerators would be required in the following few years. None was built because the whole cement industry was soon burning waste derived fuel. The lobbying activity of one of the incinerator companies was much more effective than that of the cement industry, which had done no lobbying at that stage. Many of the public difficulties faced by Castle were symptoms of an industrial battle fought out behind the scenes, a battle that the cement industry eventually could be said to have won. One measure of that success is that over the last ten years the cement industry, and Ribble in particular, has moved from being seen as an environmental problem to being seen as part of the solution.

Bart Marsden by Loch Lomond, returning from a delivery to Skye

Frequently, several members of the same family have worked for Ribble. Take the Pollard family for instance. Ernie Pollard was an overhead crane driver. His sons Bob, shift manager, David, shift fitter, Bruce, shift chargehand and Ernie, storeman, joined their father at the works. Ernie senior was often heard to say, 'Any chance of a job for the wife?'

Hans Riley, retired transport foreman

Hans Riley retired in 2005. He came to Grindleton from Holland in 1955 when he was just 10 years old. From an early age he wanted to be a lorry driver but you had to be 21 years old. When that day came he went to see the transport manager, Arthur Jones, and asked for a job. On five successive occasions he was asked to come back the following week, but finally he heard the reply he wanted 'start on Monday'. No special licence was required in those days.

Hans married Carol, whose father was Stanley Richmond, then transport foreman. At one time the cement works was a family affair, Hans, Stanley, Carol in accounts and Stanley's wife Olivia in the canteen.

In the late 1960s Stanley lived in the house nearest the garage, now occupied by computer services. When there was a queue of trucks waiting at any time of night he would come out of his house in his pyjamas to direct traffic and sort out weight tickets.

Working hours for drivers were long, up to eighty hours per week. In 1978, during the construction of the Kielder dam (1976-1982), Hans would often spend the whole week in Northumberland, transferring cement by lorry from Pressflow wagons at Hexham rail depot to the dam construction site. He stayed at the Mariners in Acomb, where he almost became part of the family. One memorable week it snowed at Kielder on the Monday so he was told to wait at the Mariners until the next day. The following morning so much snow fell locally that he thought his wagon had disappeared. He and Johny Jones spent the whole week in the hotel with nothing better to do than clean the landlord's kitchen in exchange for feasting on his T-bone steaks.

In 1971 Hans collected a brand new ERF wagon, registration LWB 156K, from Ketton. Flat out he could just achieve 37mph, so he was back in Clitheroe within the week. Two years later, and with Hans running short on patience, the vehicle was fitted with a larger fuel pump and top speed increased to a bone shaking 55mph. When Hans retired, as transport foreman, he had completed almost forty years service with the Company.

From the start up of kiln 7 in 1983 quite a few local people considered the plume from the stack to be unacceptable. Even though dust and gaseous emissions were consistently within statutory limits the plume was hazy and sometimes highly visible, especially when high winds looped it down towards the ground. In the early 1990s Peter Walker, chief engineer, had wind tunnel tests done at Salford University and as a result permission was obtained to raise the height of the stack by 15 metres. Dispersion was improved but the visibility remained an issue, so with use of Cemfuel being an issue too it was eventually decided to fit an exhaust gas scrubber just prior to the stack. The scrubber was the first fitted to a UK kiln and was installed when Ian Sutheran was general manager. It was an outstanding success and remains so;

Paul Livesey wins Huddersfield marathon in about 1978

on warm days the plume is invisible, although on cool, moist or misty days the steam in the emission condenses and a short plume can then be seen.

Every year Ribble makes contributions to local charities and sponsors events such as the 5th November fireworks display in the grounds of Clitheroe Castle. In 1995 Ribble made a contribution to the installation of CCTV in the town, one of the first such installations in the country. An official breakfast opening by the chief constable of Lancashire, the first female chief constable, was arranged. At the last minute the then Home Secretary, Michael Howard, decided that he would do the honours. As part of the event the Ribble Valley Borough Council had arranged a buffet breakfast. Michael Howard was duly offered the local delicacy, a bacon buttie. With a withering look he replied, "I am a Jew". Whoops!

Bellman quarry received approval in 1996. Castle employed Hal Moggridge OBE VMH PPLI FIHort RIBA AAdipl, as landscape architect, to help with the planning application. He is past president of the Landscape Institute, a member of the Architectural Panel of the National Trust and in 1999 was awarded the Victoria Medal of Honour by the Royal Horticultural Society. On top of all that Hal is a charming man and we have been very fortunate to have him work with us.

Paul Livesey, who joined Ribble in 1964, became chief chemist for the whole Company. He was a member of the UK working group on EN196, the European standard for cement test methods. Most important for Ribble he was on the alkali silicate reaction working group of the Concrete Society; this work in the 1990s resulted in a reduced alkali limit for cement and significant environmental improvements and cost savings for cement manufacturers. Paul was also the UK cement industry's representative on European Committee for specification of cement and lime. In his youth Paul was a marathon runner, running 4,000 miles per year in training. His best time was an astonishing 2 hours 17 minutes, then an Olympic qualifying time; despite this performance there were more than ten other English runners with faster times. In Paul's works manager days

Nick Dinsdale, leading a hill climb

The team that took part in the 10km HeidelbergCement Jubilee Run in Maastricht, 2006. Left to right: Chris Punchard, Duncan Westlund, Maria Punchard, Gareth Price, Luke Keighley

he caught Mick O'Rourke cleaning a car in the loco shed when he should have been working. "What are you doing Mick?" he said, "Cleaning my car," said Mick. "Well you can have three days off and clean it properly at home," said Paul and suspended him for three days.

Nick Dinsdale, purchasing manager prior to taking early retirement, was another of Ribble's talented athletes. In

Ronnie Blair, electrical foreman

1993 he was north Lancashire road club open champion, achieving amongst other things a distance of 253 miles on his road cycle in 12 hours. In Cyclo-Cross he won the national veterans championship in the 1994/5 season and in both those years won the Three Peaks event. Nick obtained a degree in sports therapy in his spare time and has worked as team masseur for the GB and English cycling teams. He now runs a private practice in Clitheroe.

Danny Coulston started as a mechanical apprentice at Ribble and was promoted, via kiln manager at Ketton, to become general manager of Padeswood in the critical years of the building of the new kiln there.

Paul Higson and David Holgate, apprentices of the year in 2006 and 1977 respectively

David Holgate, who is now engineering manager, was regional apprentice of the year in 1977. In 2006 Paul Higson emulated that feat when he was awarded apprentice of the year for the northwest region of Training 2000. The works currently employs eight apprentices and is planning to recruit several more this autumn.

Gareth Price started as an electrical apprentice at Padeswood and came to Ribble as general manager. He led the site through the tricky transition to single kiln operation. In 1990 Castle had set out to operate three works, each with highly efficient dry kiln production processes, each with first class standards of

25 year service award dinner, June 2007, left to right Frank Whaites, Michael Hall, Bernard Marsden, Gary Young, Mohammed Ilyas

environmental performance and each using alternative 'waste derived' fuels to replace a significant proportion of the traditional fuel, coal. The closure of the wet kilns marked the final stage in the achievement of those Company goals.

The recent appointment of Gary Young to the position of general manager brings us up to present. Gary's father Martin had worked at Ribble for over twenty years when Gary started as an electrical apprentice in 1983. For many years Gary worked in the electrical department, under the close guidance of Ronnie Blair.

He subsequently worked his way up the management ladder through a variety of jobs, including process engineer, quality manager and production manager, all at Ribble. His goals are to achieve world class performance standards in all aspects of cement production. At Christmas apprentices have traditionally had to sing carols in the works canteen. It is already clear to all that Gary is a far better manager than he was a carol singer, so the scene is set for a bright future.

Tommy Hargreaves, shot firer, Lanehead quarry

M6 over River Lune at Lancaster

A9 Killiecrankie bypass

Chapter 8
The Future

One day, long in the future, the quarry will be worked out and cement making will finish, bringing to an end well over 400 years of industrial operations on the site.

After the achievement of the mid 1990s planning permission the project team, including Iona Mander (company secretary), Brian Greenwood (solicitor and planning specialist) and Hal Moggridge climbed Pendle Hill to celebrate, followed by a good lunch at the Assheton Arms at Downham. Over a beer they mused over how long it would be before the final restoration, with lakes filling the two quarries, would be complete. Recalling that a few opponents of the planning application had claimed that birds in the Ribble valley had been wiped out by fumes from the chimney stack, Peter del Strother penned the following poem.

The cement maker

From Pendle Hill I watch the break of day.
Across the valley floor the parting night
Rolls back to show the dappled silver-grey
Cement works standing in the morning light.

No noise nor dust are there and I can see
And hear the birds, which darting here and there
Sing out the wondrous joy it is to be
Upon the wing, at dawn, in scented air.

Oh what fantastic art, that man has found
His place to work in such a landscape true,
A means to win the stone from out of ground
And make so little hurt to sound or view.

And when the stone is gone and all is done
Two lakes will grace our Ribble Valley dear.
And, on the water, children having fun
Will hardly know that we were ever here.

What is certain is that the cement works will operate for many years to come and that the people who work there will continue to play their part in the local community. Clitheroe, with its still flourishing 'Law, Lime and Latin', has much to look forward to.

Model of cement works and surrounding area showing the lake after the quarry has been restored. It was produced by S M Haywood, landscape architect, for the late 1960s planning application. The model was restored and used again for the mid 1990s planning application when permission was obtained to reopen Bellman quarry

Bee orchid in restored limestone grassland at Lanehead quarry

APPENDIX A
Bibliography and other sources

Bold Venture, 2003.
Unpublished study by Naomi Kennerley

Calcareous Cements: Their Nature, Manufacture and Uses. Gilbert R Redgrave and Charles Spackman. 3rd edition 1924. Charles Griffin and Co Ltd

The Cement Industry 1796-1914, a history. Major A J Francis. David and Charles

Clitheroe Advertiser and Times and its predecessors (microfiche in Clitheroe library local history section)

Clitheroe in the 17th Century. William Self Weeks. Clitheroe Advertiser and Times

Clitheroe 1000 Years. Langshaw

Clitheroe, 2005. Published by Clitheroe Town Council. Printed by Ribble Valley Borough Council

Clitheroe Castle – a Guide, 2006. David Best. Carnegie Publishing Ltd

Clitheroe in the Old Coaching Days, 1897 and 1929 Stephen Clarke. Clitheroe Advertiser and Times

Clitheroe in the Railway Days, 1900. Stephen Clarke. Clitheroe Advertiser and Times

Daily Herald 1949

Daily Telegraph 1987

English Heritage. NMR

History, Directory and Gazetteer of Lancashire 1824. Edward Baines

How Cotton came to Clitheroe. Langshaw. The Borough Printing Company, Clitheroe

Industrial Development of Upper Ribble Valley (thesis). P D Newman. Clitheroe Library Local History

Industrial Heritage, 1990. Mike Rothwell. Bridgestone Press

Lancashire Record Office, Preston

Lancashire 1939-1945 The Secret War. Ron Freethy. Countryside Books 2005

Lead Mining in the mid-Pennines, 1973. A Raistrick

Leicestershire Record Office, Leicester. (home to a great deal of information on Ketton, Ribble, Horrocksford and Bold Venture)

Ribblesdale works archives and photograph archives

Some Vanishing Homesteads of Clitheroe. 1955. Langshaw. The Borough Printing Company, Clitheroe

Some writers on lime and cement. Charles Spackman. 1929. W Heffer & Sons Ltd

Southampton City Heritage Services. Alastair Arnott, curator of local collections

The Old Inns and Alehouses of Clitheroe, 1947. Arthur Langshaw. Published by Kaydee bookshop

The Pendle Witches. Walter Bennett, 1957

Victoria County History of Lancashire

APPENDIX B
Employees, February 2008

Last Name	First Name	Length of Service	Job Title
Ainsworth	Carl	8	LGV driver
Armitage	Martin	20	LGV driver
Astin	David	22	Quarryman
Ball	Stephen	26	LGV fitter
Ballance	Thomas	24	Process operative
Barker	William	27	LGV driver
Barnes	Brian	6	LGV driver
Barrett	Patrick	22	LGV driver
Bate	Stephen	32	Training supervisor
Bates	Adrian	7	Regional business development manager
Beer	Steven	38	Assistant co-ordinator
Blockeel	John	33	Mechanical supervisor
Blockeel	Francis	41	Workshop co-ordinator
Boardman	Frank	7	LGV driver
Boushear	Kenneth	7	LGV driver
Bowen	David	8	LGV driver
Bowen	John	24	Fitter
Bowen	Stephen	13	LGV driver
Bowman	Lee	10	Process controller
Bowman	Glenn	5	Concrete laboratory assistant
Braithwaite	John	7	Concrete laboratory supervisor
Braithwaite	Edward	29	LGV driver
Braithwaite	Terry	18	Senior buyer
Brewer	Mark	20	LGV driver
Bridges	John	29	LGV driver
Brierley	Douglas	6	LGV driver
Bristow	Michael	11	LGV driver
Brodie	David	30	Area manager
Bulmer	Ian	11	LGV driver
Burgess	John	19	Quarryman
Burnop	Peter	28	Quarryman
Cambridge	Daniel	8	IT support engineer
Cann	Gavin	4	Quality and development manager
Chadwick	Daryl	11	Electrician
Chapman	Lee	9	LGV driver
Chew	John	8	LGV driver
Clish	Stephen	11	LGV driver
Compton	Peter	9	LGV driver
Cook	Patrick	8	LGV driver
Cottam	Paul	9	Welder/fitter
Court	Colin	10	LGV driver
Cowell	Paul	6	Mechanical engineer
Cowking	Michael	33	Electrician
Cowking	Graham	31	LGV fitter – team leader
Cox	Raymond	33	LGV driver
Crosby	Robert	5	LGV driver
Cross	Allan	29	Despatch team leader
Dabbs	Kevin	4	LGV driver
Davidson	Stuart	10	Key account manager
Davies	John	6	LGV driver
Davy	Robert	25	Process engineer
Dean	Dereck	21	Planner
Dean	John	8	LGV driver
Dinsdale	Howard	30	Fitter
Dixon	Derek	30	LGV fitter
Dixon	Philip	2	Assistant distribution manager
Dixon	Christopher	9	IT business analyst (SAP)
Docherty	John	7	LGV driver
Driver	Luke	3	Apprentice (electrical)
Duckworth	Howard	18	IT manager
Dugdale	Martyn	10	Process operative
Duxbury	Neil	13	LGV driver
Duxbury	Paul	6	LGV driver
Eadie	Andrew	22	LGV driver
Eastham	David	10	LGV driver
Eatough	Ronnie	24	Process – team leader
Eddleston	Andrew	5	LGV driver
Edmundson	Stephen	28	Process operative
Elliott	Dale	11	LGV driver
Ellis	Anthony	30	Process controller
Ellison	Philip	5	LGV driver
Embley	David	31	LGV driver
English	Andrew	17	Service desk co-ordinator
Entwistle	Paul	11	Workshop manager
Fagan	Georgina	8	Planning administrator
Fenton	Timothy	9	Electrician
Ferguson	Kevin	10	Process operative
Ferguson	Anthony	7	LGV driver
Fielding	Peter	9	Shift manager
Fish	Christopher	28	Safety health environment advisor
Foster	Michael	11	LGV driver
Fox	Anthony	35	Fitter
Gallagher	Leonard	12	LGV driver
Garigan	James	23	LGV driver
Gaskell	Frank	19	LGV driver
Gaskill	David	16	Fitter
Ghosh	Jane	5	Chemist
Gillies	Derek	1	Traffic planner
Gladwin	John	19	Welder/fitter
Gormill	David	16	Distribution supervisor
Gorton	Gary	6	LGV driver
Grainger	Tom	2	Apprentice (mechanical)
Grainger	Carol	10	System and demand administrator
Green	Annette	19	Safety and quality manager
Greenwood	Janet	14	IT support assistant
Grimshaw	Jonathan	4	Production trainee
Grooby	David	22	Fitter
Gudgeon	Alan	10	Process analyst
Hall	Michael	27	Process controller
Hall	Thomas	5	Quarry operative
Halstead	Christopher	7	LGV driver
Hardy	Martin	11	LGV driver
Hargreaves	Thomas	29	Shot firer/explosives supervisor
Harris	Craig	1	Electrician
Harrison	Bernard	13	LGV driver
Hart	Richard	4	LGV driver
Hartley	Stephen	21	Accountant

Employees, February 2008

Last Name	First Name	Length of Service	Job Title
Harwood	Mark	12	LGV driver
Harwood	Philip	7	LGV driver
Haworth	Derek	13	LGV driver
Haworth	Christopher	30	LGV driver
Haworth	John	28	Laboratory analyst
Haworth	Neil	7	LGV driver
Haycock	Ronald	12	LGV driver
Heaton	David	29	Quarryman
Higham	Paul	9	Process operative
Higson	Paul	5	Reliability engineer
Hind	Paul	24	Process operative
Hindle	John	13	LGV driver
Hodgkinson	John	15	LGV driver
Holden	John	25	Welder/fitter
Holgate	David	31	Engineering manager
Holgate	Zakariyya	2	Apprentice (electrical)
Hoole	Barry	35	National fleet engineering manager
Horne	Janet	2	Human resources assistant
Hosker	Christopher	20	Welder/fitter
Hothersall	David	30	Operations supervisor
Hothersall	Deborah	8	Purchasing stores clerk
Hothersall	Daniel	6	LGV Apprentice
Howard	Ian	30	LGV driver
Howard	Vanessa	21	Secretary to technical department
Howard	Thomas	3	Apprentice (mechanical)
Howarth	Matthew	30	Electrician
Humphreys	Gill	28	IT support manager
Hunter	Sheree	12	Administration assistant
Ilyas	Mohammed	27	Process operative
Ingham	Grant	35	LGV fitter
Jackson	Nolan	8	LGV driver
Jackson	David	22	Electrician – team leader
Jefferson	Nicholas	11	Team leader distribution
Johnstone	Allan	22	LGV driver
Jones	Anthony	7	LGV driver
Jones	Carl	7	LGV driver
Jordan	Kirk	9	LGV driver
Kabrna	Peter	13	LGV driver
Kearton	Leslie	6	LGV driver
Kehoe	Michael	6	LGV driver
Kent	Leslie	7	LGV driver
Kenyon	Graham	28	Fitter
Kenyon	Paul	10	Process controller
Kenyon	Lisa	4	Part-time distribution clerk
King	Benjamin	17	Operations supervisor
King	Matthew	28	Fitter
Lafranceschina	Joseph	24	Despatch operative
Lafranceschina	Karen	8	Buyer
Lake	Trevor	1	Business analyst
Latham	Malcolm	25	Process controller
Lesczynsky	Anthony	28	Process analyst
Limbert	Leslie	15	LGV driver
Lloyd	Derek	35	Electrical supervisor
Loi	Andrew	9	Process operative
Lonsdale	Lynnette	39	Distribution secretary
Mackenzie	Steven	21	Laboratory technician
Maher	Steven	10	Process operative
Maidman	Alan	11	LGV driver
Malone	Keith	35	Fitter
Malone	Robert	35	LGV driver
Marcella	David	19	Despatch operative
Marchant	Stephen	4	Planner
Marsden	Joseph	11	LGV driver
Marsden	Bartholomew	19	LGV driver
Marsden	Bernard	27	Process analyst
Marsh	Andrew	10	Process operative
Martin	Robert	22	LGV driver
Mason	Kerry	21	Distribution manager
Mason	Christpher	29	LGV driver
Mason	Andrew	9	Process operative
McBride	Joseph	29	Process – team leader
McCallion	John	4	LGV driver
McGee	Mark	7	LGV driver
McGrath	Cathryn	6	Administration assistant
Mcintosh	Alastair	10	Planner
McLean	Alastair	34	LGV driver
McLean	Roy	41	Planner
McVeigh	Anthony	4	LGV driver
Meadows	Adrian	8	LGV driver
Menzies	Paul	17	LGV driver
Menzies	Christopher	1	Laboratory technician
Mills	Gordon	19	LGV driver
Mitchell	Norman	18	Systems engineer
Monk	Sue	2	Trainee scientist
Moore	Andrew	8	LGV driver
Moores	Keith	12	LGV driver
Moorhouse	Simon	11	Quarry manager
Moorhouse	Richard	5	LGV driver
Morrison	Allan	5	LGV driver
Muir	Russell	4	LGV driver
Munro	Alexander	7	LGV driver
Murdoch	William	23	LGV driver
Murray	Chris	30	Mechanical supervisor
Murray	Anthony	19	Application services project leader
Musgrove	Mathew	4	Trainee scientist
Musgrove	Stephen	36	Quarryman
Myers	Gifford	39	LGV driver
Myers	Keith	40	LGV driver
Nash	Paul	23	LGV fitter – assistant team leader
Naylor	Kevin	36	Despatch operative
Nelson	Peter	29	Shift manager
Nerenberg	Eric	35	Quarryman
Nerenberg	Peter	29	Quarryman
Nerenberg	Robert	1	Apprentice (electrical)
Nicholson	Ben	12	Electrical engineer
Nicholson	David	10	LGV driver
Nixon	Michael	30	Quarryman
Nowell	Michael	8	Process operative

Employees, February 2008

Last Name	First Name	Length of Service	Job Title
Nuttall	Oliver	4	Apprentice (mechanical)
O'Brien	Michael	1	Depot attendant
Parkinson	Lucy	21	Purchasing/stores manager
Parkinson	Neil	7	LGV driver
Passmore	Alexander	4	LGV driver
Patchett	Nicholas	34	fitter
Peel	Edward	8	LGV driver
Pepper	Stuart	23	Northern technical manager (commercial)
Perkins	Mark	12	LGV driver
Phillip	Christopher	14	LGV driver
Pickersgill	John	18	LGV driver
Plant	Graham	27	Supervisor distribution
Pollard	David	40	Fitter – team leader
Pomfret	David	34	Electrician
Prentice	Shaun	7	LGV driver
Preston	Keith	14	LGV driver
Punchard	Christopher	28	Process analyst
Punchard	Maria	21	Secretary to general manager
Purcell	Gary	12	LGV driver
Raeburn	Edward	23	LGV driver
Rawcliffe	David	13	Shift manager
Rawnsley	Martyn	4	Apprentice (electrical)
Rayner	Sam	1	Apprentice (mechanical)
Reeve	Michael	6	LGV driver
Richardson	Francis	6	LGV driver
Rushton	Brian	28	Auxiliary (garage)
Salisbury	David	19	Laboratory analyst
Scott	Gary	30	Laboratory supervisor
Seed	Mark	19	LGV driver
Seed	Graham	8	LGV driver
Sharp	Paul	10	IT support assistant
Sharpe	Nick	23	SHEQ manager
Shepherd	Kevin	15	Traffic planner
Sherwood	David	13	LGV driver
Shuttleworth	David	12	Electrician
Simpson	Tom	24	Planner
Smalley	Frederick	38	Electrician
Smith	Eric	14	LGV driver
Smith	Gordon	10	LGV driver
Smith	Peter	4	LGV driver
Southall	Alan	5	LGV driver
Steer	Charles	7	LGV driver
Stevenson	John	14	Systems engineer
Stoddart	George	35	LGV fitter
Stubbs	Roger	34	Fitter
Sweeney	Clifford	36	Process – team leader
Taylor	David	10	LGV driver
Taylor	John	8	LGV driver
Taylor	Adrian	5	LGV driver
Taylor	Andrew	16	LGV driver
Telese	Frank	30	Fitter – team leader
Thompson	Michael	31	Fitter – team leader
Thompson	Michael	5	LGV driver
Threlfall	Alan	29	Stores attendant
Tilley	Nigel	13	LGV driver
Tillotson	Andrew	10	LGV fitter assistant team leader
Tillotson	Robin	29	Despatch operative
Tinker	Jonathan	5	Traffic planner
Todd	Steven	32	Electrician
Tomlinson	Steven	25	Despatch operative
Tomlinson	Chris	26	Technical services manager
Tonner	Jody	4	Area sales manager
Townley	John	9	Welder/fitter
Townson	Robert	35	LGV fitter/team leader
Townson	Emma	2	Maintenance administrator
Turner	Brian	30	Process – team leader
Turner	Steven	11	Process controller
Vanderson	Ernie	11	LGV driver
Vest	Robert	7	LGV driver
Walker	Nicholas	8	LGV driver
Walker	Peter	7	LGV driver
Walmsley	Bernard	18	Electrician
Walmsley	Geoffrey	30	Weighbridge attendant
Walton	Andrew	11	LGV driver
Ward	Russell	7	LGV driver
Watson	Simon	9	LGV driver
Wellock	Derek	30	Welder/fitter
Westell	Christopher	8	LGV driver
Westwell	Christine	3	Part-time distribution clerk
Whaites	Frank	27	Process operative
Whalley	Jason	7	Laboratory technician
White	Timothy	10	Distribution auxiliary
White	Nigel	1	Analyst programmer
Whittaker	Dale	24	Electrician
Whittaker	Paul	37	Process analyst
Whittaker	Michael	13	Stores attendant
Wilkinson	Roderick	25	Laboratory analyst
Willcock	Anthony	4	Planner
Williams	David	14	LGV driver
Wilson	Sean	23	Shift manager
Wilson	John	28	Fitter – team leader
Wilson	Andrew	6	LGV driver
Wilson	David	18	LGV driver
Wood	Michael	10	Process – team leader
Wood	David	5	LGV driver
Woodhead	John	26	Laboratory manager
Woodruff	David	26	Process analyst
Woodworth	David	25	Despatch operative
Wormleighton	Jon	1	Area sales manager
Worthy	Andrew	1	Shift manager
Wrathall	Sam	9	Operations supervisor
Wrathall	Daniel	0	Quarry operative
Wyllie	Angus	23	LGV driver
Yates	Lee	18	Maintenance analyst
Young	Gary	25	General manager (production)
Zamorski	John	19	Stores – team leader

APPENDIX C
25 Years Service Employees

The following individuals both current and past have all achieved 25 years service or more. Special mention should be made of Fred Smithson, the only person to achieve 50 years service.
This list has been compiled from old photographs, personal memories and more recent personnel records.
We apologise for any omissions.

Last Name	First Name	Last Name	First Name	Last Name	First Name	Last Name	First Name
Adamson	George	Bywater	Eric	Edmundson	Stephen	Hillary	David
Adcroft	Thomas	Cairns	Harry	Eglin	Arthur	Hitchin	John
Adderley	John	Carlyn	Sammy	Ellis	Anthony	Hitchin	Bill
Ainsworth	John	Catchpole	Adrian	Ellse	Keith	Hogg	Ken
Akbar Khan	Ali	Catlow	Dick	Embley	David	Hogg	William (Bill)
Akroyd	Tony	Catlow	Martin	Evans	Ronnie	Holden	Jim
Amin	Mohammed	Chadwick	Ian	Exton	David	Holden	John
Armstrong	Sid	Chadwick	John	Ferguson	Gerald	Holgate	Robert David
Aspin	James	Chappell	Arthur	Ferguson	John	Hoole	Barry
Aspin	Ron	Charlton	Brian	Fern	Barbara	Hothersall	David
Azam	Sikander	Chatburn	Bernard	Fielding	Terrance	Hothersall	Bob
Baker	Les	Chatburn	George	Fish	Christopher	Houlker	Derek
Ball	Stephen	Choyce	Clifford	Forster	Leslie	Howard	Ian
Banks	Ted	Coleman	James	Forster	Wilfred	Howarth	Albert
Barker	William	Conchie	Les	Fowler	David	Howarth	Matthew
Barnowski	Stanley	Cottam	Rodger	Fowler	E	Hussain	Mam
Barron	Harry	Cottam	Roger	Fowler	Ned	Hutchins	Heather
Bashir	Mohammed	Cottier	Simon	Fox	Anthony	Ilyas	Mohammed
Bate	Stephen	Cowking	Graham	Garlick	Jim	Ingham	Grant
Baxter	Arthur	Cowking	Michael	Garner	Leonard	Isherwood	John
Beer	Steven	Cowperthwaite	Richard	Gatti	Silvano	Johnson	Brian
Bennett	Mark	Cox	Raymond	Geldard	Peter	Johnson	Ian
Bialecki	Martin	Crane	Kathleen	Gilbert	Billy	Johnson	Keith D
Billson	John	Cross	Allan	Goodbier	Michael	Jones	Bob
Binks	Jack	Cross	Richard	Graham	Phillip	Jones	John
Birchenough	John	Crossland	Ted	Greenwood	Antony	Jones	Tom
Birchenough	Judith	Darbyshire	Ian	Grooby	William	Jones	Arthur
Bithell	Bill	Davy	Robert	Guy	Peter	Jordan	Frank
Blair	Ronnie	Dean	Sid	Hacking	Tom	Kelly	Tom
Bleasdale	Peter	Demain	Bill	Hall	Keith	Kenny	John
Blockeel	Francis	Dewhurst	Paul	Hall	Michael	Kenyon	Graham
Blockeel	John	Dickinson	Chris	Hall	Anne	Khan	Fatroz
Bond	Marjory	Dinsdale	Howard	Halliwell	Grenville	Khan	Mulik
Boyer	Clarry	Dinsdale	Nicholas	Hamilton	David	King	Matthew
Boyer	George	Dixon	Derek	Hampshire	Graham	Kitching	W D
Bradley	Michael	Dixon	Jack	Hargreaves	Robert	Kleszcz	Henry
Braithwaite	Hamby	Dixon	Les	Hargreaves	Thomas	Korol	Will
Braithwaite	John	Dixon	Steven	Hargreaves	Tishy	Kozlowski	Tadeusz
Brewer	Alan	Dixon	Bill	Hargreaves	Edgar	Lakin	William
Bridges	John	Dooris	Fredrick	Hart	Doug	Latham	Leonard
Briggs	Frank	Downham	Bill	Hart	Alfred	Latham	Malcolm
Brodie	David	Downing	Michael V	Hartley	Eric	Latter	Billy
Brotherton	Alan	Dowson	Frank	Haworth	Christopher	Lesczynski	Kazimierz
Broughton	John	Drage	Robert	Haworth	John	Lesczynsky	Anthony
Burgess	Alan	Drake	Richard	Heaton	David	Lewis	Ronnie
Burgess	Eric	Drews	Marian	Hebson	John	Livesey	Paul
Burnop	Peter	Dubowski	Alex	Heslin	Phillip	Lloyd	Charlie
Bush	David	Duckworth	Bernard	Hewitt	Wilfred	Lloyd	Derek
Butt	Andrew	Dunbabbin	Trevor	Hill	Gordon	Loi	Amedeo

Last Name	First Name
Lonsdale	Lynnette
Malone	Keith
Malone	Robert
Manning	John
Mantle	Roy
Marchese	Giovanni
Marsden	Arnold
Marsden	Bart
Marsden	Bernard
Mashiter	Arthur
Mason	Billy
Mason	Christpher
Mason	Terence
Mcbride	Joseph
Mccally	Kevin
McGrath	Paul
McGurk	Frazer
McLean	Alastair
McLean	Roy
McLernon	Brian
McTear	Trevor
Meadows	Don
Medd	Austin
Moon	Geoffrey
Morris	Rawdon
Murray	Chris
Musgrove	Stephen
Myers	Gifford A
Myers	John
Myers	Keith
Nash	Lionel
Nawaz	Mohammed
Naylor	Kevin
Nedeljkovic	John
Nelson	Peter
Nerenberg	Eric
Nerenberg	Ewald
Nerenberg	Peter
Nicholas	Jack
Nicholas	Ralph
Niven	Norman
Nixon	Jeff
Nixon	Michael
Nowak	Ludwig
Nutter	Jimmy
Oddie	Albert
O'Hare	Patrick
Parker	Donald
Parkes	Fred
Parkes	Peter
Parkinson	John
Parkinson	Norman
Parkinson	Robin
Patchett	Nick
Pickering	Kevin

Last Name	First Name
Pickover	Alan
Pickvance	Norman
Pietrzak	Thomas
Pinch	Albert
Plant	Graham
Pollard	David
Pollard	Robert
Pomfret	David
Pratt	Doreen
Procter	Tom
Punchard	Christopher
Punchard	Dennis
Pye	Harvey
Read	Doug
Riazat	Mohammed
Rice	Michael
Richards	James
Richmond	Stanley
Ridgway	John
Rigg	Frank
Riley	Hans
Rimmer	John
Roberts	Richard
Robinson	Brian
Robinson	Geoffrey
Robinson	Harry
Ronzino	Joe
Rothwell	John
Rung	Alf
Rushton	Brian
Russell	Wally
Rutherford	George A
Salisbury	Peter
Salisbury	Steven
Saul	Matt
Scott	Alan
Scott	Gary
Scott	Margaret
Seed	John
Seedall	Alan
Seroka	John
Sharp	Fred
Sharples	Fred
Sharples	Harold
Sharples	Bill
Sherliker	Derek
Sherliker	Wilf
Sherwood	Robert
Shuttleworth	Raymond
Shuttleworth	Walt
Simpson	John
Sims	Alan
Sims	John
Singleton	J Kenneth
Smalley	Frederick

Left to right: R F Stagg, Fred Smithson (50 years service), R Y Parkinson, J H Billson and Mackintosh

Last Name	First Name	Last Name	First Name
Smalley	Tom	Tyne	Terry
Smith	Alan	Waddington	George
Smith	Edwin	Waddington	Jim
Smith	Ginger	Wakeling	George
Smith	William J	Walker	Billy
Smithson	Fred	Walker	Peter
Smithson	John	Walker	Tot
Sowden	Malcolm A	Wallace	Samuel
Speak	Arthur	Walmsley	Geoff
Stacey	Ted	Walton	Tommy
Stagg	Rawson	Webster	Alf
Steed	John	Webster	Sydney
Steer	Terence	Wellock	Derek
Stirling	Alan	Wells	William
Stoddart	George	Whaites	Frank
Stubbs	Roger	White	Brian
Sunderland	Tony	Whitehead	Alan
Sweeney	Clifford	Whitehead	Percy
Sweitlik	Peter	Whittaker	Frank
Talese	Leo	Whittaker	Paul
Taylor	Roy	Wigglesworth	Harold
Taylor	Wilf	Wilkinson	Arnold
Telese	Frank	Wilkinson	Rod
Telese	Pasqalino	Wilson	David
Thompson	Derek	Wilson	John
Thompson	Michael	Winterbottom	Thomas
Thompson	George	Woodhead	John
Thorner	Billy	Woodhead	Robert
Threlfall	Alan	Woodruff	David
Tillotson	Robin	Woodworth	David
Todd	Steven	Worthington	Bert
Tomlinson	David	Wright	A John
Tomlinson	Geoff	Wright	Carole
Tomlinson	Keith	Yakoob	Mohammed
Tomlinson	Steven	Young	Gary
Tomlinson	Walter	Young	John
Townson	Robert	Youngs	William
Turnbull	Andy	Zarzycki	Ken
Turner	Brian		

CASTLE CEMENT
HEIDELBERGCEMENT Group

CASTLE CEMENT

CASTLE CEMENT CASTLE CEMENT CASTLE CEMENT CASTLE CEMENT CASTLE CEMENT CASTLE CEMENT
CASTLE CEMENT CASTLE CEMENT CASTLE CEMENT CASTLE CEMENT CASTLE CEMENT CASTLE CEMENT CASTLE CEMENT
CASTLE CEMENT CASTLE CEMENT CASTLE CEMENT CASTLE CEMENT CASTLE CEMENT CASTLE CEMENT CASTLE CEMENT
CASTLE CEMENT CASTLE CEMENT CASTLE CEMENT CASTLE CEMENT CASTLE CEMENT CASTLE CEMENT CASTLE CEMENT
CASTLE CEMENT CASTLE CEMENT CASTLE CEMENT CASTLE CEMENT CASTLE CEMENT CASTLE CEMENT CASTLE CEMENT
CASTLE CEMENT CASTLE CEMENT CASTLE CEMENT CASTLE CEMENT CASTLE CEMENT CASTLE CEMENT CASTLE CEMENT
CASTLE CEMENT CASTLE CEMENT CASTLE CEMENT CASTLE CEMENT CASTLE CEMENT CASTLE CEMENT CASTLE CEMENT
CASTLE CASTLE CASTLE CASTLE CASTLE CASTLE CASTLE